Antonio's Will

Yasmin Tirado-Chiodini

Antonio's Will

Yasmin Tirado-Chiodini

Black Hammock Books
Black Hammock Enterprises, LLC
Oviedo, Florida, U.S.A.
www.blackhammockbooks.com

This is a historical work of fiction based on a true story. Most of the real names of the persons and places involved in the story have been preserved due to their historical value. Many allusions to the characters' thoughts, dreams, interactions, and communications are fictional. Please refer to "Author's Note" for general information on research sources.

ANTONIO'S WILL. Copyright © 2014 by Yasmin Tirado-Chiodini.

Published 2014 by Black Hammock Enterprises, LLC
ISBN: 978-0-9817307-7-6

12 11 10 9 8 7 6 5 4 3 2 1

Dedication

To

Tom and Isabella
Raúl Tirado Gracia Pontón, M.D.
The Pontón family and their descendants

Contents

Acknowledgements

I am indebted to my father for the Pontón legacy. I wish I could share the discoveries with you, Dad.

Thank you, Tom and Isabella, for allowing me the time to embark in this journey and for your endless love and support.

Thanks to family and friends, my sounding boards during this project.

My sincere gratitude to all those who provided feedback on this novel at various stages, I value your time and insight.

To the staff or members of the organizations I consulted, some of which I address in the Author's Note, your guidance, resources and professionalism made a difference.

And to my source of inspiration, wherever you may be, thank you for the legacy.

Foreword

She researched when everyone slept. In the dead silence, her mind worked with more clarity. No interruptions, no worries. Sometimes she even imagined that her ancestors guided her. That they reached out from the past to share their stories.

"Hocus Pocus!" she thought, smiling. Her inside joke was a source of inspiration.

But her imagination was not far-fetched.

My second cousin, twice removed, is a family historian. She is also a lawyer. And this is why I chose her. I needed her to do me a favor. I chose her, although she is a business lawyer and not a criminal lawyer. That was fine by me. It's not like my lawyers did a superb job at defending me. I was wrongfully executed.

One night, I urged her to stay up later than usual to dig deeper into the Pontón line. She had diverted her attention to research another line on her tree, but I made her revisit mine. I insisted she focus on my name.

"José Antonio Pontón Santiago," I whispered at her, repeatedly.

Antonio Pontón, for short.

"Keep researching Antonio!" I urged her. "Please keep digging! It is important!"

I compelled her to investigate further. And she did.

"Hocus Pocus?" she whispered with an inquisitive frown. This time she was half-joking.

If you asked me, I think she knew I was there, standing next to her, peeking over her shoulder. But I digress. At the very least, she had a feeling that she was onto something.

When she found out, disbelief set in. My story had not been passed down to her family. My story was buried when they buried me.

"Why?" she wondered. "This is big! Why?"

She asked, "Why?"

The weight was lifted off my shoulders. I left her alone to ponder. No need to frighten her. I had accomplished my goal. She knew what she had to do next. I would be there if she needed me to help. Her silent assistant.

It was now in her hands to unearth the details of a story so painful that it was hidden from history. It was in her hands to investigate, to connect the dots. And I trusted her. I knew she would represent my case well. One hundred years later.

I knew that when my story surfaced, she would tell it. She would be compelled to redeem the reputation of a man wronged by injustice. She would have to restore my family's name. This much I owed my father Manuel, after all his sacrifice, and my mother Etervina, after the suffering I caused her. They now know everything.

But the world never knew!

My sorrow and regret for the crime I committed have followed me into eternity.

I walked my new lawyer through my journey, so she could walk you through it. This is my story, and to understand it, you have to know my father's story, because my will, my free will and my legacy, are entwined with his life and with the history of my beloved island of Puerto Rico.

You be the judge. One hundred years later.

José Antonio Pontón Santiago

Prologue

They called him "Ponce de León" because he acted as though he could conquer anything and anyone. He enchanted every young woman that came his way with *piropos* (pick-up lines) and clever sweet talk.

"Has spring started? I just saw the first flower!" Antonio whispered as he walked by a group of blushing young ladies, tipping off his white *Panama* hat as a silent 'How do you do?'

He was never at a loss for words.

"What are you doing out this morning? Don't you know that stars only come out at night?" was one of his favorite lines. And he had many.

On a good day.

Men in town regarded him with admiration. "How does he do it? How can he charm the ladies so?" they thought. Maybe they could learn a thing or two from José Antonio Pontón Santiago, so they could also capture some female attention, even if for a split second.

Antonio Pontón, for short, could be a charming man. Wearing the latest fashion, perfumed, shaven and barbered, he always carried plenty of money. Regardless of his whereabouts, his native Puerto Rico or in New York, when it was time to pay, he would pull out a roll of tightly wrapped bills from his right pocket and start counting his blessings. Once, a fellow student saw him draw $300, quite the fortune in 1912, especially for a student. Antonio made sure he displayed his bills long enough for all to see. He relished being the center of attention.

But being showered with attention can sometimes be a curse.

The ash-blond, green-eyed *conquistador* was one of five children born into a wealthy family from the town of Comerío in Puerto Rico. The tropical island had become a territory of the United States in 1898, when Antonio was a young boy. As a result of the Spanish-American

4

War, under the *Treaty of Paris*, Spain transferred Puerto Rico to the United States, and Puerto Ricans have been undergoing the transition ever since, caught between two worlds.

"Fitting in" could be a never-ending process for many, even for well-to-do Antonio. Behind his confident façade, he struggled to reach harmony with his own family and friends.

And with himself.

Despite his charm and wealthy upbringing, harmony was not in the cards for Antonio.

Antonio's father, Manuel Pontón Fernández, was born in Spain and migrated to Puerto Rico in 1870 at the young age of 14, fleeing the deteriorating Spanish economy and fueled by dreams of opportunity. Manuel worked his way up with enormous sacrifice, became one of the most prominent tobacco planters in the island, married and raised a beautiful family. He had "made it," and he swore that his children would never have to endure the adversities he had suffered.

But Manuel never saw his son's fate coming. He had not a clue that his son Antonio would become a murderer, and that his life would burn into night and the grave.

Part I. From Asturias to Puerto Rico

Asturias, Patria querida, Asturias de mis amores;
¡Quién estuviera en Asturias en todas las ocasiones! ...

Asturias, my beloved Motherland, my loved one Asturias;
Who could be in Asturias for all times! ...

- A Segment from the Anthem of Asturias, Spain
(Said to have been composed in Cuba)

~

La tierra de Borinquen ... es un jardín florido de mágico primor ...
Es Borinquen la hija, la hija del mar y el sol ...

The land of Borinquen ... is a flowery garden of magical beauty ...
Borinquen is the daughter, the daughter of the sea and the sun ...

- Segments from "La Borinqueña" poem,
composed in 1903 by Manuel Fernández Juncos and
adapted as Puerto Rico's Anthem in 1952

Chapter 1. El Asturiano Pontón

Manuel Pontón Fernández was born *circa* 1856 in the province of Oviedo, Spain in a small town called *Viyao* (also known as *Villar.*) The town is part of *Borines*, one of the 24 parishes of the *Concejo de Piloña* situated in the North West of Spain. *Borines* is in *Infiesto*, the capital of *Piloña*. This northwestern region of Spain is also known as *Asturias*. Back then Piloña had a population of about 16,000 inhabitants and Infiesto about 3,000. These numbers decreased over time as a result of the vast migration of Asturians to the Americas.

Manuel came to this earth at a time of great turmoil in Spain, a country still suffering the ripple effects of Napoleon Bonaparte's invasion in the early 19th century. In 1814, the Spanish War of Independence resulted in the expulsion from Spain of Napoleon and his brother Joseph, whom Napoleon had installed as King of Spain. In 1815, Spain enacted *La Real Cédula de Gracias* (The Royal Decree of Graces), a law geared to open the channels of commerce and grant incentives to Spaniards seeking fortune in the colonies. From 1815 to 1836, the law helped populate and farm Spanish land in the so-called *Indias*. As a result of the decree, many Spaniards left their loved ones behind in Spain for a chance at opportunity in the colonies.

Through the years, the Spanish *Madre Patria* (motherland) established a strong connection with its colonies. Many *Indianos* (as the locals called those who had migrated to "the Indies") became wealthy through hard work in the territories and returned to Spain to give back to their communities. They created employment and built schools, as well as beautiful homes or *casonas*. They also infused their towns with a culture of betterment, inspiring everyone, particularly the local youth.

The *Indianos* were living proof to their families that higher aspirations could yield rewards. "Achieving the dream" was possible,

9

despite the lingering political instability following the Bonaparte ousting in 1814, which continued to rip Spain apart.

When Manuel was a young boy, a future in Spain remained unclear for many, but there was hope in America.

. . .

In 1870, when Manuel was about 14 years old, ships to La Habana, Cuba and San Juan, Puerto Rico navigated on a regular schedule from Spain. Many Spanish newspapers advertised the promising journey. One such ad ran in the *Boletín Oficial de Oviedo*, a local periodical published by the government, which printed the ads every day. The ad published on Friday, January 8, 1870 read:

"Peninsular line steamboats will connect with mail vessels of D. Antonio López and Company, capable of carrying about 3,000 to 3,500 tons of weight, and they will stop in Avilés or Gijón to pick up passengers en route to Puerto Rico and La Habana. Passengers will be transported to Cádiz and will embark in the mail steam vessels that will depart on the 15th and 30th of every month with destination to La Habana. These vessels provide the utmost comfort and sleeping accommodations in bunk beds for the trip from Cádiz to La Habana. Passengers will receive the best treatment by intelligent and nice Captains during the happy 16 or 17-day trip. Whether traveling to or from these destinations, passengers will receive the utmost consideration. The Company will provide travel and meals for the price of only 50 duros, which covers from the moment the passenger embarks in Avilés or Gijón to the final destination in La Habana or Puerto Rico. However, if the passenger, for whatever reason, should remain in Cádiz for a few days waiting for the steam vessel connection to La Habana, they shall be responsible for the cost of said wait. The responsible party in Avilés, Mr. Feliciano Suárez, will provide all information to interested parties. Mr. Suárez also issues first-class, second-class and third-class tickets to Puerto Rico and La Habana, such that passengers can secure their place in the connecting vessel. Third-class passengers who travel by land directly to Cádiz will receive a discount on their ticket. – Suárez"

- Boletín Oficial del Principado de Asturias (Official Bulletin of the Princedom of Asturias) No. 4, Friday, January 8, 1870

Antonio López y López, the man behind the transatlantic ship company mentioned in the ad, first established his company with his brother in colonial Cuba in 1847. *Antonio López y Hermano* did business with ships traveling between the colonies. It began operations with a 400-ton hybrid sailing ship side-wheel steamer. In 1857, he formed a naval company in Alicante, Spain, under the name of *Compañía de Vapores Correos A. López,* to establish a regular steamship line between Cádiz in Spain and Marseilles in France, featuring intermediate stops along the way.

In 1861, Antonio López y López won the Spanish government bid and concession for sea transport of mail and passengers between Spain, Puerto Rico and Cuba. It commissioned new ships for that purpose, subsequently extending its routes. Antonio López received the noble title of *Marqués de Comillas* (*Marquis of Comillas*) in 1878. Through the years, his company became the respected *Compañía Transatlántica Española* and even assisted Spain with auxiliary vessels during the Spanish-American War in 1898.

In 1870, the price of the steamship fares to Puerto Rico from Oviedo, Spain was about 50 *duros* or 250 *pesetas*, which estimated to modern unskilled wage was equivalent to about $6,800 and based on GDP was equivalent to approximately $1,200. This was a massive expense for middle and low-income families, particularly those with many children.

Due to the high cost of travel, it was not unusual for families to send their young children alone to join relatives or friends who already lived in America. Young Manuel was among these. His father José Pontón Figaredo traveled to Puerto Rico before him. Manuel stayed behind in Spain with his mother María Fernández Sánchez, his sister Carolina and the rest of the family. Some time after Manuel's mother María passed, José sent for his son. Carolina, already married and settled, remained in Infiesto.

Manuel was made aware of the challenging trip to America from those who had traveled there before him. He knew that the transition was not without difficulty. Still, he was determined. As he prepared for his journey, his leaving Asturias and the rest of his family haunted him.

But he was young.

Chapter 2. Manuel's Asturias

The waters of the Atlantic Ocean and the Celtic Sea met to kiss the northern shore of Asturias. The beautiful Cantabrian Mountains protected the south. Manuel's Infiesto was infused with exquisite natural beauty, where abundant green mountains and small valleys combined with the bluest sky into the most perfect landscape. The climate was humid and temperate. There was plenty of rain, bountiful rivers like the *Piloña*, and natural wonders, including caves, such as *La Cueva de Sidrón*. The Asturian land provided for a wide variety of trees, including apple, oak, chestnut, hazel and eucalyptus. This remains the same today.

People in Manuel Pontón's hometown made their livelihood through agriculture and livestock, but Asturias' seafood had no equal. Even so, Manuel's favorite dish was the traditional *Fabada Asturiana*, a rich stew that originated in the 16th century. It was made with large white beans, pork, and two types of sausage (black *morcilla* and spicy *chorizo*.) Asturians also enjoyed drinking *sidra* (apple cider), the region's traditional alcoholic drink (which Manuel would get a hold of from time to time, even at his young age), and the mouth-watering *Cabrales* cheese, the green-blue creamy delicacy. They still do.

Farmers in Infiesto lived simple and often long lives. It was not unusual to find a man who would still work the land at 90 years old, set in his faith and his ways, a strong work ethic first and foremost, anchored in the belief that God would send him a sign when He wanted him to stop. Many farmers did not know how to read or write, but their wisdom and character far made up for their lack of literacy.

While the younger generation strived to avoid the war, others searched for "the promised land," and perhaps unbeknownst to them, a complicated and not necessarily happier existence.

They just wanted more. And who could blame them? The grass was greener elsewhere, as some say, especially when political instability threatened the future. They dreamed about the New World, having lived amid a legacy of centuries of history.

The rich Asturian heritage in Manuel's ancestry dated to the earliest of times. The Celtic influence permeated through the music (with sounds of the Asturian bagpipe or *gáita*) and also the people's physical appearance. Many of them were of light skin, hair and eyes. The Celtic roots also showed in their language. Before Asturians spoke *Castilian* Spanish, they spoke *Asturiano* or *Bable*, a language derived from Latin with Celtic influence. They still speak it.

The Roman influence in Asturias (during 29-19 B.C.) was evident. Ancient Roman bridges and structures continue to pepper the land today. And since the mountains did not appeal to the Moors, kings saw in Asturias a convenient site for refuge. They left behind the bequest of their many castles and palaces, as ornaments to embellish the landscape of the Kingdom of León.

As with many other Spanish towns, countless church structures dating back to the 8th Century blessed Asturias. The *Catedral de Santiago de Compostela* (Cathedral of the Apostle St. James), which began construction in the year 1075, houses the remains of *Santiago Apóstol* (the Apostle St. James). It is the end point for the famous *Camino de Santiago* (Way of St. James) pilgrimage from all over Europe. *La Santa Cueva de Covadonga* (Holy Cave of Covadonga) in the northwest of Asturias guards the remains of *Pelayo* (Pelagious), the first King of Asturias, who died in 737 A.D. and claimed to have seen the Virgin Mary at the cave. An ancient statue of *La Virgen de Covadonga* (The Virgin of Covadonga) remains at the site commemorating the sacred occasion. This is also the locus of the famous Battle of Covadonga, where the King's troops defeated the Moors. In 1901, the Basilica of Covadonga was consecrated in the site of the original shrine. Closer to Manuel's Infiesto was the *Catedral de San Salvador* (Cathedral of the Holy Savior), founded on 781 A.D. These ancient historic structures still stand today as an integral part of the every-day local life and attract much admiration from visitors.

Family, friends, sights, food, ancient culture, and rich history. There was much to miss, and there was no telling of when, or if, Manuel would ever return home to his Asturias.

What would become of his life in the *New World*?

Chapter 3. Journey to Puerto Rico

To save, young Manuel traveled by train all the way from Infiesto in the north of Spain to his southern port of departure in Cádiz. The journey by land took well over 14 hours. Manuel's body was not strong. He was a scrawny blond, green-eyed, short and freckled young man. But his mind possessed all the strength he needed. He learned to be resilient and resourceful.

"*¿Ayudáis al débil?* Can you help a weak fellow?" said young Manuel in Castilian upon his arrival to Cádiz, clever to enlist the assistance of other passengers to help him carry his trunk.

"*¡Subíd por la cuesta! ¡Hay un atajo! ¿Lo veis?* Let's drag it uphill! There is a shortcut! Do you see it?" he instructed his "assistants." Other passengers were doing the same, so the helpers agreed to drag the luggage uphill from the station through the shortcut to the port, as requested.

His trunk was not so heavy. Manuel packed some basic items: a hat, a cap, one pair of black boots, three pairs of pants, a jacket, a blanket, three pairs of socks, six pairs of underwear, six shirts, six undershirts, one set of sheets, two towels, and six handkerchiefs. He carried on his person 150 *pesetas*, his boarding ticket to San Juan, his birth certificate and his visa.

"*¡Muchísimas Gracias! ¡Que Diós se lo pague!* Thank you so much! May God repay you!" Manuel said to the men who helped him, tipping his *boina* (beret). "*¡Nos vemos adentro del barco!* I will see you inside the ship!"

"*Principe Alfonso*," he read the name of his ship out loud, as he scanned the vessel from left to right. "There you are!" He smiled, his eyes wide-open.

"*¡Impresionante bestia!* Amazing beast!" Manuel said. "Let's see if we make it alive!" he chuckled with sarcasm, overcome by mixed feelings of excitement and fear of the unknown.

The *Principe Alfonso* was built in the United Kingdom in 1863 for the naval company of *Antonio López y Compañía*. It was 3,475 tons of dead weight, measured 281.2 x 32.1 x 18.7 feet, and it had a capacity for 1,010 passengers.

"*¡Con permiso!* Excuse me!" Manuel said, as he squeezed his body through the crowd surrounding the vessel. "*¡Ay madre! ¡Qué de gente!* Oh, mother! So many people!"

There were families saying their farewells, passengers loading the mixed luggage, lovers sharing their last embrace, and people troubleshooting issues with their ticket or documentation.

After he boarded, an attendant pointed him towards his room, which he would share with three other passengers. The arrangement in third class was two bunk beds per room.

Manuel would spend over two weeks at sea replaying memories of everything he had left behind in his hometown of Infiesto and wondering what was to come. He endured an unbearable seasickness triggered by the rocking cargo vessel and the foul smells around the ship. But he arrived in one piece to San Juan and to his final destination, the small town of Comerío.

Soon after, he mailed his first letter back home.

"Comerío, Puerto Rico, January 31, 1870

My Dear Sister Carolina and Family,

I have arrived to the island of Puerto Rico safely after what I must confess was probably the worst travels a human being has ever endured. It is my opinion that the best punishment for a criminal would be to send him across the ocean on a trip like the one I just completed. Traveling in the cargo steam ship was sickening. I cannot even imagine how those traveling to Argentina can outlive the thirty-five days of sheer torture. I must thank God that I only had to suffer through fifteen days at sea.

At the beginning, the Principe Alfonso (my ship) did not behave so badly. The first day you could see how people were loading all sorts of musical instruments: violins, flutes, guitars, an accordion, even a gáita. These passengers must have learned that the travels were rough and wished to add some cheer to their journey. Everyone went to sleep after the first night of music and dancing. But we did not know what was coming the day after we departed. The ocean was not calm, quite the contrary. There were giant mountains of water surrounding the ship, rocking it and shaking it in every possible direction. I could hear people becoming ill all over with each movement of the vessel (myself included), and the sound and smell of it all was unbearable. It calmed down some when we stopped in Canarias, but then the anguish commenced all over again.

Many passengers said that if they could turn the ship around and go back to Spain, this is what they would prefer. Some would somehow endure the seasickness better than others; mostly the people in Third Class. Obviously, misfortune has weathered us and made us stronger than most of those in First Class. The sleeping arrangements left a lot to be desired. I do not wish to describe the food, which we could not eat much of in any case, because we were sick a great portion of the time. I mostly drank liquids for the first six days, as my stomach could not hold solids.

One good thing is that from time to time, when the sea became calmer, you could hear the music and go dance with the other passengers. They were very cheerful, and they were playing the gáita. This made it much easier for me to bear the journey.

During the travels and seasickness, I had time to think about my blessings and how I must take advantage of the opportunity that has been given to me. I give thanks that I am now in firm land, safely. Upon my arrival to Comerío, father and others were there to offer a warm welcome. This is a very green land with mountains that remind me of Infiesto. However, it is extremely hot and humid here, although the mountain breeze is most enjoyable.

I promise my actions here will make you all proud.
I will try to write often.

Your,

Manuel Pontón Fernández"

Young Manuel's reading and writing skills were not the best. He dictated his first letter from Puerto Rico to his father José, who wrote it and sent it on his behalf.

Chapter 4. Alejandro Villar, Count of Laviana

M anuel knew that he was bound to the town of *Comerío* before he left Asturias. His father José had settled in the neighboring town of *Bayamón* with a new wife and young family. José arranged that upon Manuel's arrival he work as a clerk at the local *tienda mixta* ("all purpose" store) of a family friend, Alejandro Villar y Varela, who was baptism godparent to some of José's Puerto Rican children.

Alejandro Villar was an Asturian businessman from the town of *Miyares* in Infiesto who arrived in Puerto Rico in 1866 at the age of 18 and became Mayor of Comerío in 1879. He was a short and stocky fellow with not much hair left, rose-colored cheeks and a big strawberry-blond combed moustache that gave him a distinguished air. *El Señor Alejandro* looked impeccable, and always dressed with suit, tie and hat. His hard work and perseverance, and his participation in the Spanish military and the Chamber of Commerce in the island afforded him a high reputation with local businesses and with the Spanish Crown. As a result, he was able to amass a respectable fortune.

Manuel was wise beyond his years, and he was also hardworking and ambitious. As soon as he saved enough money, he took it upon himself to employ a tutor to enhance his reading and writing skills, and his overall knowledge of the island. Villar witnessed Manuel's initiative, dedication and great success potential. He knew Manuel was special, and he became Manuel's mentor, teaching him everything he knew about business.

One day, when Manuel had saved enough to make an impression, he took a chance. He fixed his green eyes on Villar's and said, "*Señor Alejandro*, I want to buy your store."

And Alejandro Villar, without hesitation, said, "*¡Pues a tí sí te la vendo!* Well, yes, I shall sell it to you!" and he sold the store to Manuel.

After working in his *tienda mixta* for some time, young Manuel invested everything he could in purchasing land, drawn to the promise of the tobacco business. Although its early economy included coffee and produce, Comerío was known as one of the best regions in the island for tobacco planting due to its rich soil and its proximity to the *La Plata River*.

Manuel acquired as much land as he could afford and refused to sell it to anyone, even if he was not planting anything on it.

"La tierra no se acaba" ("the land does not perish"), he often said.

In 1894, Manuel Pontón appeared on the island's business directory along with other renowned *industriales* (businessmen), including Alejandro Villar. That same year, Pablo Ubarri Capetillo passed away, leaving his position as President of *El Partido Incondicionalmente Español* (The Unconditionally Spanish Party) in Puerto Rico vacant. Also a Spaniard, Ubarri was born in 1824 in a town named Santurce (Santurzi), located in the northern region of Vizcaya. In 1839, he arrived in Puerto Rico with a Royal concession to develop railroads in the colonies. He also owned land in the island and had a variety of businesses. In 1880, Ubarri developed the steam tramway from *Plaza Colón* in San Juan, passing through Miramar, to the town of Río Piedras. That year, he received the noble title of *Count of San José de Santurce,* and the area of *Cangrejos* in the Miramar sector of San Juan changed its name to *Santurce*. In 1898, the *Puerto Rico Railway Light and Power Company* acquired the steam tramway and by 1900, it had converted it to electrical power. The famous area of *El Condado* in San Juan is named after the land Ubarri once controlled.

Due to his excellent reputation as an honest and hardworking businessman, as well as a Spanish loyal, Alejandro Villar was called to fill Ubarri's vacant role. Villar had big shoes to fill, but he did so well. In 1896, Queen María Cristina of Austria, the second wife of King Alfonso XII of Spain, honored Villar with a noble title. He became *conde de Laviana* (Count of Laviana).

A few months after the Spanish-American War of 1898, *el conde* Alejandro Villar, by then a wealthy and successful nobleman, returned to Infiesto, becoming one of the legendary Indianos in the area. There, he built a beautiful home (which he named *Villa Villar*, today known as *Les Camelies*), a school, a chapel and helped expand the local cemetery, among other contributions. He also had a retreat in Gijón he named *Villa Puerto Rico*, where he spent some of his retirement time.

Don Alejandro and his wife, Matea Alicea Méndez, had children while in Puerto Rico. Their son Eduardo Villar Alicea, born in Comerío in 1879, remained in the island to run his father's business affairs. After Alejandro Villar passed, Eduardo inherited his noble title and continued the family's relationship with Manuel Pontón.

And so, not only had Manuel Pontón Fernández become a planter and an emerging businessman, he also had strong connections with Spanish nobility.

Chapter 5. The Pearl of La Plata

Comerío was different from Infiesto, but in some odd way it was reminiscent to Manuel of his homeland. The town rested in the northern area of the island's *Cordillera Central* (Central Mountain Range), extending for about 28.22 square miles.

"Tell me about the history of Comerío," Manuel asked his tutor, Rafael, when he first hired him.

"Well, Manuel," the tutor began. "The town has more than one name, not just Comerío. When they founded it in 1826, they called it *Sabana del Palmar* because of the royal palm trees in the area. The name later changed to Comerío after a local *Taíno Indian* Chief. *Comerío* was the son of *Chief Caguax*. We locals sometimes call it *La Perla del Plata* (The Pearl of La Plata) because the *La Plata River*, the longest river in Puerto Rico, runs through the town."

"Its valleys remind me so much of Asturias," Manuel said.

Comerío was blessed with vivid green landscapes, rich soil, and plenty of rain, like Manuel's Infiesto. It was not difficult for him to be endeared to Comerío. As different as it was from Infiesto, it felt so familiar.

Manuel adapted well to the Puerto Rican culture and its African and *Taíno Indian* influences, which permeated into the local language. *Taíno* words such as *tabaco* (tobacco), *barbacoa* (barbecue), *canoa* (canoe), and *hamaca* (hammock) remain in use today in Spanish, English and other world languages. Also, the word cigar or *cigarro* is derived from the *Taíno* word *sik'ar,* a Taíno gathering or festival where tobacco played a main role.

"Some of the local people still have *Taíno* features," Manuel observed.

"They sure do," said Rafael. "The *Taíno Indian* blood still runs through the veins of many of the islanders. Some Spanish and African people have intermarried with Indians, so although the *Taínos* are extinct as a people since the *Conquista*, you can still see *Taíno* in the faces of some of the locals."

"They are beautiful people, with such lustrous hair and copper-colored skin," Manuel said.

"Many of the local Spanish descendants also have tanned skin, but you know, their skin color comes from working under the sun for so many hours," said Rafael. "Some foreigners can't tell the difference. They don't care to learn about our roots, our history, what made us who we are today. So, we become responsible to learn about our history, like you are right now, and to pass it on, to make sure that it is not forgotten."

Manuel nodded as Rafael spoke. He also took notes on a small notebook that he carried everywhere.

"The *Taínos* were one of the *Arawak* peoples of South America, indigenous to the Bahamas, Greater Antilles, and the northern Lesser Antilles, well before *Cristóbal Colón* (Christopher Columbus) arrived," said Rafael. "They inhabited the Island of Puerto Rico, which they called *Borikén*, or *The Island of the Great Lord*. *Agueybaná I*, which means *The Great Sun*, was the *Cacique* or Chief in Puerto Rico at the time of its discovery on November 19, 1493 during Columbus' second voyage. *Agueybaná* greeted *conquistador* Juan Ponce de León upon his arrival in 1508, but he died in 1510. His brother *Agueybaná II* replaced him, and he also fought Spanish subjugation."

"They were brave men, the *Taínos*. At first, they welcomed the Spanish in peace, but when their welcome was abused, they fought, and this brought on their demise," said Manuel, realizing the irony.

"Unfortunately, yes," the tutor continued. "The *Taínos* soon perished as a people from slavery and infectious diseases carried by the Spaniards, such as smallpox, to which the *Taínos* had not been exposed until the arrival of the conquistadors."

"It saddens me to learn how people who had been living here for centuries were quick to perish at the hands of the conquistadors," said Manuel.

"History repeats itself, as some say."

"*Maestro* Rafael, I must confess and beg your pardon, but when I came to Puerto Rico, I was a little scared of the Africans."

"I have heard that often!" the teacher chuckled. "It is normal to fear the unknown. But people are just people, in all shapes and forms. Black people have a different culture and beliefs, and we must respect that and try to understand. Slavery has left deep scars. They have led a difficult life. Many of them were abused. They lost their dignity as human beings. But not all Africans came to Puerto Rico as slaves, you know?"

"I have heard that some Africans lived in the south of Spain as free men, although many were enslaved. They never made it to Asturias, though. At least I never saw any colored people up north, not even Moors," Manuel said. "I did see some when I traveled to Cádiz, though, on my way to *América*."

"You heard right, Manuel," the tutor confirmed. "The earliest Africans came to Puerto Rico as free men accompanying the Spanish conquistadors. The first African man to arrive in Puerto Rico in 1509 was Juan Garrido, a conquistador who traveled with Juan Ponce de León. Garrido was the son of a King born on the West African coast. He fought alongside the Spaniards to subjugate the *Taínos* into slavery. Garrido later went on to fight in Mexico at the side of *conquistador* Hernán Cortés."

Manuel interrupted, "So you are telling me that an African man helped a white man conquer the Indians. Strange alliances. I guess everything centers around power."

"Most of the time!" Rafael smiled. "But they were not always at war. They fell in love with each other, too! Pedro Mejías was also another free African man who accompanied Ponce de León's troops. Mejías married *Yuisa*, a female Chief Taíno or *Cacica*. The African trade began in the islands after the enslaved Taíno Indians perished. It was well underway by the mid 1500's, and the rest, well, you know the rest."

"It is just wrong to enslave a human being. It seems we keep making the same mistakes through history," said young Manuel.

"Yes, the same mistakes," said Rafael. "People die and take their lessons-learned with them. The new generations repeat past mistakes. Slavery dates back thousands of years, yet it is ever present in our lifetime. The *Taínos* also suffered attacks by the *Caribe Indians*, and they enslaved the Taíno women and children. In modern slavery, some Africans enslaved other Africans, and even helped Europe and the Western world obtain slaves. They acted as brokers, human traffickers of their own race, selling their own people! Many of those enslaved were people from enemy tribes, who the African dealers kidnapped and sold to white slave traders."

Manuel shook his head left and right.

"This is not evident to many people. Africans selling Africans. Africans enslaving Africans. But it happened," Rafael continued. "Some people think that somehow God made them to be better than others because of the color of their skin, the tribe they belong to, their country of origin, or the amount of riches they have. But God made us all the same," said Rafael. "For some reason we tend to use religion to excuse acts that God would not approve. But these are man's actions here on Earth, and we should accept responsibility for them."

"How could the Roman Catholic Church support slavery?" asked Manuel. "I mean, I heard that that when ships full of slaves arrived at the Port of San Juan not so long ago, every slave had to be baptized, or else he or she could not be sold."

"True. I think the church saw it as an opportunity to save souls. They thought that the Africans were being saved by baptism, a new religion, and were assured employment to live a better life," said Rafael. "But this is a simplistic perspective. No one cared to understand that what the African slaves left behind was most valuable to them: their families and their culture. They were not animals, like cattle. They were humans. People who supported slavery never anticipated or cared about the hurt caused by it. The abuses. The horror of it all. Because Africans looked different and acted different, they were deemed to be of a lesser race. Because they did not share the same beliefs, 'they needed to be saved.' This behavior was driven by ignorance."

"I know of children who had to work at the service of the man who actually paid for their trip to the colonies. This is another form of slavery," Manuel said. "Fortunately, my father was able to pay for my trip and arrange for my employ with *El Señor* Villar, where I earn a salary."

"That is called *Indentured Servitude*, and some say it is another form of slavery because of the many abuses committed with the *indentured servants*. You are fortunate your father was able to pay for your trip," Rafael said.

"It is a good thing that we have departed from slavery," said Manuel. "I know it impacted the pockets of slave owners, but it is a price our society had to pay to do what is right."

"The Spanish Crown offered a transition plan, but the transition has been challenging. People don't just walk away from slavery and integrate into society in one day. It is going to take time, years, perhaps centuries, no one knows. And much work and patience from both sides. A great amount of patience," said Rafael.

"I understand," said Manuel. "We are so different in so many ways. It is difficult to believe that we could all somehow get along and even intermarry when we are so different, but I am seeing signs here that this is possible."

"It is not so difficult to understand, when you live on a small island and have the same goals as your neighbors. To have a home, food, and a family. To be happy. Our basic wants and needs are not so different after all," said Rafael.

"This is true," said Manuel. "But some of us want more than others!" he added, revealing his vein of ambition.

"Just remember, Manuel," said Rafael chuckling. "I can see that you are an ambitious young man. You can strive for more, and this is good, but when you reach your dreams, when you have your land, your family, and you have workers, remember to treat them with respect, no matter where they come from. We all need one another. We are all creatures of God."

Rafael was a wise teacher. He knew first-hand. He descended from African slaves.

. . .

In his early lessons with Rafael, Manuel also learned that the African and Taíno influences were a strong component of the Puerto Rican cuisine (*cocina criolla*), as well as the local art, music and literature. Puerto Rico had stunning flora, as did Infiesto, and its food was diverse and exotic, influenced by foods originating from Africa, India, South America, and the Pacific, in addition to Spain.

"Roots such as the *yautía* (cocoyam) and *yuca* (cassava), *ñame* (taro); fruits like *guanábana* (soursop), papaya, *quenepas* (limoncillo), *guayaba* (guava), and *piña* (pineapple); grains like *carillas* (black-eyed peas) and *maíz* (corn); and spices such as *ají* (small pepper), *recao* (spiny cilantro), and *achiote* (annatto) were integral components of the Taíno Indian nutrition. *Cacao* (cocoa) was also indigenous to the Amazon region of the Americas and has been consumed in Puerto Rico for many years," said Rafael.

"I know that the Spanish brought the coconut palm trees to

Puerto Rico from *Islas Canarias* (Canary Islands), and that these were originally from Africa," Manuel said. "But what other fruits and vegetables are in the island, and where did they originate from?"

"The *chayote* (prickly pear), *aguacate* (avocado) and *mamey* (sapote) originated from Mexico. The *caña* (sugar cane), mango and tamarind were from India, and the *patata* (potato) came from Peru. The *jengibre* (ginger) came from *Oceanía* in the Pacific via Mexico. The *pana* (breadfruit) also came from the Pacific, and the *parcha* (passion fruit) from the Amazon. The *plátano* (plantain) and the *guineo* (banana) came from Africa in the early 1500's; the *café* (coffee), the *kimbombó* (okra), the *gandúles* (pigeon peas) and the *guinea* hen arrived in the 18th century, also from Africa," said Rafael.

"The African and Taíno influences in Puerto Rican food are very prevalent," Manuel observed. "More than I ever anticipated."

"Yes, there are many dishes with African and Taíno Indian flavors. The *alcapurria* is a fritter made of mashed plantain, *yautía* and/or *yucca* stuffed with a variety of meats or fish. The *pasteles* are similar to the *alcapurria*, but these are wrapped in a plantain leaf tied with a string and boiled, not fried. The *mofongo* is made with fried green plantain mashed with garlic," said Rafael.

"I noticed people deep-fry foods quite a bit here in the island," said Manuel.

"Yes," said Rafael. "The African slaves introduced the practice of deep-frying food."

"I was pleased to see that they eat *tostón* here. It is one of my favorite dishes!" Manuel said.

"Here they call it *lechón asado*," said the tutor. "They roast a pig on a stick on an open fire, like in some places in Spain."

"Delicious!"

. . .

As time passed by, Manuel traveled to San Juan for business affairs, and he visited *La Mallorquina*, a Spanish restaurant established in *Calle San Justo* in 1848. There, he could eat typical Spanish dishes, such as the *Paella* rice dish, and delicacies such as the *Mallorca*, a soft bun pastry covered in powdered sugar, often eaten for breakfast or as a snack.

The *Ron Pitorro* or *Cañita*, a type of moonshine beverage with high alcoholic content, was a Puerto Rican favorite. The liquid was distilled from sugar cane molasses, sometimes cured with fruit and buried for months. It was a clandestine drink, often enjoyed during festivities. The *Pitorro* rum taste was different from the Asturian *Aguardiente de Sidra* (apple cider moonshine), but its flavor was also rich.

A Spaniard living in Puerto Rico like Manuel could enjoy the local diverse gastronomy, while still being able to consume the traditional flavors from Spain. The olive oil, garlic, onions, pepper, the ham, cheese, and the fine wines were all being imported to the island from Spain for a while, and Manuel made many of these available at his *tienda mixta*.

. . .

The Spanish musical rhythms such as the *danza*, the *seis chorreao*, and the Christmas *aguinaldo* turned gatherings into celebrations and celebrations into festivities. Taíno, African and Spanish instruments and sounds brought life to the Puerto Rican music of the time.

Almost as soon as he arrived in the island, Manuel heard the Taíno *güiro*, a notched hollowed-out gourd, adapted from pre-Columbian days, creating a pleasant rhythm for dancing. African slaves introduced percussion sounds emitted by *tambores* (hollowed tree trunks covered with stretched-out animal skin) and *maracas* (gourds filled with pebbles or dried beans and mounted on handles.) These instruments framed the *bomba y plena* sounds and rhythms that the workers so enjoyed, through which they became local poets and storytellers, improvising verses while singing and dancing with joy. Familiar strings, such as the six-string Spanish classical guitar, and the *cuatro*, a guitar-like instrument with ten strings arranged in five different pairs, had become part of the local music and lyrics dear to the island's folklore and remain an important part of Puerto Rican music today.

From time to time, there was an opportunity to enjoy a *zarzuela* in the capital's theatre, a cultural center for the island. This beloved Spanish lyric-dramatic genre features spoken and sung scenes, incorporating operatic and popular song and dance. Even in the midst of the Spanish-American War turmoil, the San Juan theatre played

26

the *zarzuela* "Marina."

And then there was nature's music. The small frog the locals called *coquí* was a treasured new sound, a lullaby sung by the chanting Puerto Rican native species. Sometimes, while he lay in bed awake at night, Manuel tried to imitate the sound of the little frog. He tried to sing it at first. But then he realized he could get the sound just right by whistling it.

"*Coquí! Coquí!*" Manuel whistled. He improved his *coquí* whistle every day, until he sounded just as the little frog. People in town laughed at Manuel practicing his *coquí* sounds. Sometimes they could hear his whistles from outside the store, as though Manuel was carrying out a conversation with the small creatures.

The tiny *coquí* sang through the nights and soothed Manuel's sleep, keeping him company and reminding him that he was not alone.

. . .

With the help of his tutor Rafael, Manuel became an avid reader. He so enjoyed the writings of local authors, which emanated a strong sense of Puerto Rican identity. Their works made Manuel grow closer to Puerto Rico and its people. *El Gíbaro*, written by Manuel A. Alonso in 1849, described the *criollo* daily life. Rural speech patterns portrayed the Puerto Rican-born *criollo* view of the world and gave hope to the *jíbaros*, the rural poor, to attain education and gain employment, even in times of hardship.

The masterpieces of José Gautier Benítez (*Poesías*), Alejandro Tápia y Rivera (*La Cuarterona*), Eugenio María de Hostos (*La Peregrinación de Bayoán*), Lola Rodríguez de Tió (author of the Puerto Rican anthem *La Borinqueña* and a descendant of Juan Ponce de León) and Cuban author and activist José Martí (nicknamed "The Apostle of Cuban Independence"), along with the leadership of the authors themselves, became profound sources of inspiration to Manuel.

Puerto Rico's art was also a deep source of pride and enrichment. The art by San Juan's 18th century painter José Campeche y Jordán and Bayamón's Impressionist painter, Francisco Oller y Cestero were not only of unique beauty, but they also told the tales of the history and culture of the island, its faith and its people. Campeche was Puerto Rico's first native painter, considered one of the best rococo artists in the Americas, and Oller studied in *El Prado* and *The Louvre* museums in Spain and France, taught famous painter Cezáne, and exhibited next to Monét and Renoir, among other famous painters.

. . .

Manuel soon experienced the local traditions introduced by African slaves, such as the *baquiné*, also known as the *velorio*.

"*Señor* Manuel," said Juan Expósito, one of Manuel's workers, as he entered the *tienda* one morning.

"*Sí, Juan. Dígame.*" said Manuel. "Tell me."

Juan removed his hat and held it over his chest with both hands.

"*Perdone que lo moleste, patrón.* Pardon me for bothering you, boss, but my wife and I wanted to ask if we could use one of the empty barns to celebrate Ana's *baquiné*. It would be an honor if you could also come to celebrate with us."

"A *baquiné?*" Manuel asked.

"Señor Manuel, our baby Ana passed away last night. The doctor said it was gastroenteritis. We want to celebrate a *baquiné* before we bury her," said Juan, with teary eyes.

Their young child had died and the family was celebrating a party, instead of a funeral.

"Juan, I am sorry to hear about your baby, Ana. *¡Claro que sí!* (Of course!) You can use one of the empty barns, and I will be there. Please tell me what else I can do, whatever you all need," said Manuel, still shaken by the sad news and somewhat confused by the tradition.

"Nothing, *Señor* Manuel. Just come and celebrate with us. Ana is going to heaven!" Juan said with sadness, biting his lip, but with a strong belief.

Juan's last name was "Expósito," the last name given to newborns with unknown parents. Children were often left at someone's doorstep; sometimes with a note stating their first name and that the parents could not care for the baby. Other times, the babies were just abandoned at a doorstep or at church, without more.

The misery of poverty.

As Manuel arrived to the *baquiné*, he noticed Ana's minute body lay in an altar, dressed in white, surrounded with flowers, some fresh and some hand-crafted with colorful paper. The barn had been cleaned thoroughly.

"Juan, thank you for inviting me to your celebration," Manuel said. "Ana looks beautiful. An angel. The place looks immaculate!"

"*Gracias, Patrón,*" Juan responded. "We scrubbed every corner of the barn to be sure that Ana's spirit is not contaminated with any dirt. It's bad luck!"

Manuel noticed women were dressed in white and had headgear, while the men wore white shirts. A spiritual guide, wearing a beaded necklace with a large wooden cross began to pray the rosary, and others followed in devout and emotional prayer. Once the prayer concluded, the music, singing and dancing began.

Most of the singing was improvised. The songs told the story of the child, how she had died, and what the parents had endured to save her. Some songs revolved around her journey into the heavens, yet others spoke about the parent's mourning. The attendees performed the songs with excited gestures so that the bad spirits were exorcised from the child.

"*¡Zape!* (Shoo!) Go away, go away, *espíritu maligno* (bad spirit)!" they sang. "Go back to where you came from!"

The festive musical celebration combined the prayers and songs with expressive dancing to the rhythm of percussion and string instruments, which accompanied the child's ascent into heaven, where she would become an angel. Women, men and children ate, drank, prayed, sang and danced. They also played games like *la gallina ciega* (the blind chicken) where children tried to escape the touch of a blindfolded child who would walk around trying to feel for them. Whoever she touched was disqualified from the game.

The baquiné lasted throughout the night.

In a time when so many children perished to disease, this was a way for the child's loved ones to say good-bye and endure the painful loss. But when all were gone, the crude reality set in. Manuel will never forget the image of those poor parents, devastated, sitting alone right next to the altar where their child lay dead, weeping desperately at her loss.

He prayed for Ana's soul. He prayed for those parents.

And he prayed that he would never have to suffer the agony of losing a child.

. . .

The Spanish had brought some old and more joyous traditions from the motherland familiar to Manuel, like *La Noche de San Juan* (St. John's Night) and *Los Tres Reyes Magos* (The Three Kings), which still remain a part of Puerto Rican culture.

La Noche de San Juan takes place every year on the night of June 23. Family and friends in Spain and Puerto Rico gather at beaches to celebrate the birth of Saint John the Baptist. People enjoy music and dancing. At the stroke of midnight, those assembled at the shore walk backwards into the sea and immerse themselves in the ocean's water, back first. This is performed three times to gain *buena suerte* or good fortune for the rest of the year.

He also celebrated the *Los Tres Reyes Magos* or *Los Reyes* tradition, which still today takes place on January 6 in Spain, Puerto Rico and Latin America (as in other cultures throughout the world in one way or another, sometimes called "The Epiphany.") It extends the celebration of the birth of Jesus Christ from December 24 to January 6 and eight days thereafter, to January 13 (these eight days are known as "*Las Octavitas*" or octaves.) The tradition of January 6 represents the journey of three kings or magi from Europe, Asia and Africa. *Melchor, Gaspar* and *Baltasar* (Melchior, Gaspar and Balthasar) followed a bright star to Bethlehem to locate baby Jesus in the manger where he was born. They honored Jesus with their gifts of myrrh, incense, and gold, representing man, God and King, respectively. Each year, on the night of January 5th, children fill a box with fresh grass or hay for the Three King's camels. The camels are said to eat the grass and The Kings leave gifts for the children. This tradition is similar to the celebration of Christmas in the United States and Father Christmas in Europe, where children leave milk and cookies for the giver on December 24 and enjoy gifts he leaves behind for them on Christmas Day, December 25.

With its inherent beauty, exotic food, traditions and culture, Puerto Rico, *La Isla del Encanto* (The Island of Enchantment), the Taínos' *Borikén*, had become Manuel's home.

It was as though he had come to live in a small paradise.

Chapter 6. The Tobacco Craft

Turn-of-the-century tobacco agriculture required specialized knowledge, skill and a large investment of human capital. Manuel first learned to master tobacco farming by reading and becoming entrenched in the craft, hands-on, while operating his *tienda mixta* store.

"*¿Qué lee Señor Manuel?*" asked one of the store patrons. "What are you reading, Mr. Manuel?"

"One of my favorite books, *Manual del Cultivo de Tabaco* (Tobacco Farming Manual) by R. C. Aguayo," he proudly answered. "I am learning how to become a tobacco planter."

The book was written in 1876. Here is where Manuel first read the saying "*la tierra no se cansa*" ("the land does not get tired.") He learned that if a farmer keeps cultivating and nourishing his land, the land will provide.

"*La tierra no se acaba*," became Manuel's own saying. "The land does not perish." He was certain. "It will provide. You just have to work it the right way. It is a craft. It is a science."

Although Europeans discovered its commercial potential when Christopher Columbus brought it to Europe in 1492, it was not until the 1900's that tobacco began its commercial production peak in Puerto Rico, and Manuel would play an important role. In 1901, the town of Comerío led Puerto Rico's tobacco production with 2,000 acres of the crop planted along the *Río La Plata*, known for producing the best leaf.

The most common tobacco farmed in the valleys of Comerío was the *Hoja Prieto*, or the Dark Leaf, the best quality leaf used to wrap cigars. After Manuel acquired land, he planted the *Hoja Prieto* to maximize his profit. This type of tobacco often sold anywhere from $50 to $100 per *hundredweight* (100 pounds), while the other types of tobacco sold for much less.

Prior to 1915, a *cuerda* (about one acre) of land planted with tobacco yielded from $200 to about $600 of annual gross profits per harvest for the planter, but this amount fluctuated depending on the weight harvested, the type of tobacco processed, and the tobacco loss due to pests, disease or the weather. Sometimes, to minimize the *tiempo muerto* (dead time) and to make ends meet, planters generated two and even three harvests in one year, but the yield from the second and third harvests was of a lesser quality, and the size of the leaf was much smaller. Those who had enough land and sufficient workers could stagger the planting, weather permitting, to maximize harvests.

Expenditures were steep, and if a planter was careless, these could surpass earnings. The business had tangible overhead, labor being a large portion of expenses. Manuel never owned African slaves to work his land, since Spain abolished slavery in 1873 in Puerto Rico, three years after he arrived there. Manuel paid his laborers, whether they were former slaves, descendants of slaves, mixed, white, and whether they were born abroad or were *criollos*, born in Puerto Rico.

He never forgot what his teacher Rafael had said to him when he was younger. "Take care of your workers."

And he did.

Manuel was responsible for his workers and also for their families. Not only did he pay them for their work, but he was also their pillar for food, medical care and overall livelihood. Everyone depended on *el patrón* (the boss). They all lived in his land.

Excluding food, health and other expenditures, the cost of labor was around 70 percent of production costs. The rest would go to materials, marketing, and other expenses. About 80 percent of the total cost of production went to the processing of the tobacco leaves.

Indeed, there was not much room for profit. Manuel had to be clever about the business. He knew he had to turn his own time into money. Brokering the product and offering business services would produce additional earnings for him.

. . .

A critical aspect of tobacco planting was starting the seedlings in the *semilleros* to grow the *matitas* or small plants for later transplant to the field. Producing healthy plants from strong seedlings could pose some challenges, in part because the timing for planting the *semilleros* coincided with hurricane season, and in part because of the many pests that could invade the plants.

The months of August and September were quite rainy, and this provided the perfect environment for soil preparation. But the rain also nourished tobacco-killing weeds, fungi and insects. Before the advent of modern machinery, chemical fertilizers and pesticides that produced a better yield and decimated pests, Manuel used state-of-the-art methods and resources to maximize the successful growth of the seedlings into high-quality mature tobacco plants.

The collection and processing of the tobacco seeds themselves was a critical factor in a productive harvest. To collect seeds from a particular tobacco species, Manuel's workers selected the flowering capsules from plants for that species and covered them with paper bags so they could be dried under the sun. Prior to doing this, to avoid worm growth, they removed the flowers that had opened. After the seed capsules had dried, they cut them and stored them in a ventilated area away from the reach of rodents. They would later process the seed capsules in a *trillo* or thresher to remove all the straw, dirt and dust.

For better results, Manuel insisted on planting young seeds from a prior season but no older than two-years-old.

"*¡No quiero semilla vieja!* I don't want to plant old seed!" he reminded his workers. He was strict about that rule.

Under favorable weather conditions, Manuel's workers plowed the soil with the help of oxen or horses, once in May and again in July, when they began preparing the land for the coming season. They tilled in various directions and with different types of plows, until the soil was completely turned. Sometimes Manuel's workers would also burn the land to kill all insects and disease and any remaining weeds.

As early as the last quarter of the 19th century, Puerto Rican tobacco farmers followed guidelines such as the ones given by *The Academy of Science of Paris*, which suggested the use of chemicals, such as *naphthalene,* to eliminate insects in the field, as well as the use of nitrogen and other chemical compounds to treat the soil and kill pests in preparation for tobacco planting. The workers enriched the soil as needed, with mixtures of *abonos* or fertilizers recommended by agricultural engineers. These included natural fertilizers, such as *huano* and *estiércol,* made with bird and cow manure. Some farmers imported the *huano* from Peru, as it was said to be of excellent quality. Depending on the soil's deficiencies, Manuel would also use *abono verde* or green fertilizer made with plant compost cured over a period of months.

Semillero planting was often staggered for about 14 days to have backup plants available in case a *semillero* was compromised. To ensure proper germination, as the tobacco seeds were quite small, these were sometimes mixed with ash or sand, for easier planting and more even distribution.

After they had planted the seeds, the workers covered the *semilleros* with *paños* or "cheese cloth" to protect the young plants from the sun. They also covered the wrapper tobacco grown under shade in a similar manner, with a white canvas material. From a distance, the white canvas made the mountains appear as though they were covered with snow. The massive level of effort of the operation was striking to the human eye.

The workers often swapped the *paños* covering the *semilleros* for new clean ones, to protect the plants from disease. They watered every day, early in the morning. They watered from various directions, low to the ground, careful not to wet the soil too much, since this could spoil the plant growth.

Even though about two pounds of seed was sufficient amount to plant about one *cuerda*, potentially yielding about three to four million plants, many of these plants perished due to pests or disease. Workers had a local name for each disease infecting the seedlings. For example, among the various crop diseases were *el sancocho* (soup), caused by fungi that rotted the entire plant, *la pata prieta* (black leg), a fungus that caused root rot, and *el ojo del sapo* (frog's eye), cause for circular spots on the leaves. Also, at least eight kinds of insects invaded the tobacco crop, including the *hormiga brava* (fire ant), *la changa* (mole cricket), *el grillo* (common cricket), *el gusano cuerudo* (thick-skinned worm), *el gusano* verde (green worm), la *pulga* (flea), and *la lapa* (leech).

Once the small plants or *matitas* were ready for transplanting, around December to January, the workers moved them to the field they had prepared and planted them by hand about 12 inches apart. This was a lengthy and tiresome process, often performed in the extreme heat. They would continue to water the plants and monitor for pests and disease, as well as weeds. Sometimes, women and children helped control the pests, removing them by hand, paying special attention to the worms. Workers were careful when pulling the dead plants, which they replaced with new ones from the backup *semilleros*. They burned all the diseased plants.

Before harvesting, workers removed the outer leaves from each plant, in a process known as *desbotonar* or unbuttoning. Each plant generated about 16-18 leaves and at least four were removed from each plant, but no more than eight. This ensured good quality leaves for harvesting, as plants that grew too big could rub against others, rupturing the leaves. Also, the outer leaves were too thick and not suitable for high-quality cigar manufacturing.

The plants took about 80 to 90 days to mature, and they grew tall enough to cover a 10-year-old child. The primary harvest fell in the months of March through April. At this time, the leaves had turned from green to pale yellow and had some shine. After cutting the plants from the field, the workers sorted the tobacco plants by size, tied them in bunches with twine, and hung them upside down on long sticks positioned and different heights inside covered tobacco curing barns or *secadores* designed for drying and curing.

Manuel had the *secadores* built from east to west, to maximize the benefit of the sun and the wind. After two or three days of total cover, workers moved the tobacco bunches around inside the barn and exposed them to ventilation and some sun, as needed, to help the drying and prevent mold. This was performed with great care, so as not to break the leaves. Workers reduced the ventilation as the leaves dried. Sometimes they sun-dried the tobacco when there was no room for it in the barn, but this manner of drying yielded a tobacco of inferior quality.

Around the month of April, *despalilladores* or hand stemmers (most of them women and girls) worked the tobacco leaves with rollers, so as to compress the leaves to help "ferment" them. This practice spread the resins inside the leaf and helped reach a uniform color throughout. Fermentation could take up to 30 days.

The workers then lined up the plants and categorized them by size and quality in preparation for the *despalillo* or hand stemming. The *despalillo* consisted of removing the central vein or stem of the tobacco leaves. The *despalillador* removed half of the vein of the leaves reserved for the *tripa* or the tobacco leaves destined for the inside of the cigar; one-fourth of the vein of those destined for the

35

capote or intermediate layer between the inside and outside of the cigar; and the entire vein of the leaves selected for the *capa* or outer layer. To remove the vein, the hand stemmer used a conical metal tool or *uña*. After making incisions with the metal tool, the worker pulled the vein, careful not to tear the leaf.

They would then moisten the classified leaves with a mixture of mushed tobacco leaves, which softened and enhanced their aroma. This process was called *embetunar* or polishing. As a last step in preparation for commercial sale, the workers tied the leaf bundles with a tobacco leaf of lesser quality. The bundles were assembled into larger packages and wrapped with banana leaves in preparation for transportation.

. . .

To make the work of the *despalilladores* easier to endure and to help their focus, Manuel hired a *lector* or reader who would read books or the news out loud while the *despalilladores* worked. Sometimes he would even bring a *trovador* who would play guitar and sing. Even when his operation was well established, Manuel made his presence known in the field and the barns, especially during the *despalillado*.

"*Hay que estar presente*. You have to be present. The workers need to see you!" Manuel would say. "They need to know you care."

Manuel believed in leading by example. He also believed in teaching his workers about the history of the trade. Every time the harvest season began, the *lector* would spend a few minutes reading to the workers about the history of tobacco. He would do this, even if the workers had heard it all before.

"Tobacco was indigenous to the Americas," the reader began. "It has been growing in our land since around 6,000 years before the birth of our Lord Jesus Christ. The Taíno Indians used it for medicinal and religious purposes. They smoked the leaves, dressed wounds and relieved pain with the leaves. The word *cigar* has its roots in a Taíno celebration centered on smoking tobacco. The Taínos celebrated a periodic gathering or convention called *sik'ar*, where all the Taínos in the islands gathered, traded tobacco leaves and seeds, cigars, and coconut rum. They also discussed important matters, like land division and war against their enemy tribe, the *Caribe* Indians. They made cigars by placing a bulge of tobacco leaves in a stone mold tied with strings, which they buried until the next *sik'ar*. When the Taínos removed the aged tobacco from its mold, they would roll it inside a tobacco leaf, tie it further and smoke it."

Some workers listened. Some others chattered.

"But this is not how we do it today, right?" the reader asked the laborers, testing their attention. He would halt the reading until he received an answer.

"Right?" he repeated.

"Right!" they answered. Many of them were women and girls who giggled at the *lector*.

The reader continued. "And how did the Spanish know about tobacco?"

"*¡Por los Indios Taínos!* From the Taíno Indians!" some of the workers responded, while others said "*¡Cristóbal Colón!* Christopher Columbus!"

"Right and right!" said the reader. "On October 15, 1492, while at the Bahamas, the Taínos gifted Christopher Columbus dried tobacco leaves. After observing how the Indians used the leaves, he took some of them back to Europe, where tobacco was then grown and deemed to have medicinal properties."

The *lector* stopped reading.

"That's it for the tobacco history lesson! Great Job! Now back to work! No chit-chat!" the reader concluded with a big smile. "And now I will read the newspaper! Everyone take your seats? I won't start until everyone is seated and ready to work."

The workers chuckled, and so did Manuel, who would then wave good-bye to the *despalilladores* and leave to continue his business.

At the end of the season, farm workers removed all stubs and plants remaining in the field to prevent any fungus growth or pests. After all was removed, farm workers began to prepare the soil for the next season.

They all prayed for the hurricanes to stay *lejos*, far away.

Chapter 7. San Ciriaco

Hurricane *Santa Juana* neared in 1871, a year after Manuel's arrival to Puerto Rico. The hurricane passed about 20 miles north of the island with winds of about 120 miles-per-hour, resulting in minimal damage.

It was much different with Hurricane *San Felipe*, landing on September 13, 1876, with 100 mile-per-hour winds directly impacting the island for 10 straight hours, crossing it from east to west, devastating property and crops, and killing at least 19 people.

But the worst hurricane Puerto Rico experienced in the 19th century was *San Ciriaco* on August 8, 1899, right in the middle of land preparation for tobacco season. It had wind forces of up to 112 miles-per-hour and brought 28 straight days of rain, with 23 inches of rain in a 24-hour period. It had a diameter of about 85 miles, covering the small island that only measured 100 by 35 miles. Not satisfied with the severe losses of over 20 million dollars in property, about 250,000 homes, 90 percent of the year's crops, leveled forests, and dead farm animals, San Ciriaco claimed the largest human tragedy that Puerto Rico has ever suffered, a devastating 3,369 casualties.

The scenes in the San Juan Cemetery after *San Ciriaco* were dreadful. Hundreds of people waited in line outside the cemetery premises waiting to bury their dead, while *Pateco*, the *sepulturero* (gravedigger), would haul away the unfortunates' wooden coffins for burial, one by one, under the close to hundred-degree humid temperatures and mosquito-infested weather. When a loved one's coffin went missing–there were so many–the waiting crowd would tell the anxious relative, who was wandering around looking for its whereabouts: "*¡Se lo llevó Pateco!*" (Pateco took it away!), signaling that the gravedigger had already seized the sacred pine box to lay it in its final resting grounds. So, the famous phrase originated. Since *San Ciriaco* to date, the saying "*¡Se lo llevó Pateco!*" is often used by the locals to describe any type of misfortune, illness, accident or death.

Although Manuel and his family survived the sudden and rampant destruction left behind in Hurricane *San Ciriaco*'s path, they were not freed from loss. A month after the storm resolved to release the beautiful island from its claws, Manuel's eleven-year-old daughter, sweet Etervina, perished, a victim of *fiebre infecciosa y broncopneumonia muermoidea* (infectious fever and 'muermoid' pneumonia), a byproduct of the rampant wave of disease caused by the hurricane's floods.

Manuel's prayer at Ana's baquiné was not granted. Even when disease was so common at the time, the pain of losing a child was unbearable.

Sadly, Manuel's tragedies were not over.

Chapter 8. The Spanish-American War

"It's just a matter of time," said Manuel Pontón to the Comerío mayor and close friend, *Alcalde* José de la Rosa Carmona. "We cannot withstand the tariffs. Spain needs to relax its policies, or our businesses will not survive. No one will survive."

"You are right, Manuel," he said. "Something has got to give. People cannot keep living like this."

Over time, the internal political turmoil in Spain forced it to sacrifice its support to its colonies, resulting in their insurgence. Spain became tangled in mitigating uprisings across its territories in the Americas, and it levied taxes on most import and export of goods in Puerto Rico and Cuba in order to subsidize its internal affairs and its political supremacy efforts. By 1897, the only remaining Spanish colonies in the New World were Cuba and Puerto Rico.

Puerto Rico, as Cuba, suffered as a result of Spain's inattention to the island's needs, and it could not withstand the burdensome taxes. Many of those once encouraged to take the leap to "the land of opportunity" found themselves surrounded by disease and poverty. In addition, the new taxes placed unfair obstacles for many *industriales* who had "made it" through sacrifice and hard work. There was no incentive to continue striving for success under what was perceived as abandonment and abuse by the Spanish Crown.

"I don't see how we can continue breaking our backs, only for the Crown to overtax us," Manuel said. "I fear a revolt, like the ones thirty years ago, only more widespread."

As a direct consequence of Spain's damning policies, there were various failed revolts and manifestations by locals geared to overthrow Spain's dominance over the island, such as *El Grito de Lares* (The Lares Uprising) in 1868.

"And it has not been easy to transition from a slavery to a non-slavery economy. Spain tried to help at first, but the transition plan has not worked as anticipated," Carmona said.

On March 22, 1873, the *Spanish National Assembly* abolished slavery in Puerto Rico, three years after Manuel arrived, due to pressure from abolitionists such as Ramón Emeterio Betánces, Segundo Ruíz Belvis (both also leaders of *El Grito de Lares*), and Román Baldorioty de Castro, among others. The slaves themselves joined the cause with sheer perseverance, organizing to secure their freedom and fight the many injustices committed against them.

After the abolition, the islanders tried to implement the Crown's proposed transition plan from slavery. The slave owners received 35 million pesetas per slave, but freed slaves or *libertos* were required to continue working for three more years. Once the transition timeline ended, many of the former slaves that could not secure jobs as freed people were left to fend for themselves, joining the rest of the white and free people of color who were also unemployed or poor.

"Cuba has been negotiating its independence. Perhaps Puerto Rico will follow," said Manuel. "I am a Spanish-loyal, God knows it, but I have to feed my family and my workers. The *Madre Patria* (motherland) is not leaving much of a recourse."

Similar to the sentiment that drove the British colonies in North America to attain their independence, and following the contemporaneous initiatives for autonomy by Cuba, many Puerto Rican leaders were anxious to secede from Spain and establish their own autonomous government. A group of Spaniards living in the island (as did the *Count of Laviana*, Alejandro Villar) remained highly tied to Spain and did not feel this way, but this group was outnumbered.

"Well, let's see what happens," said Carmona. "I am unsure as to the outcome of the conversations between Puerto Rican leader Dr. José Julio Henna and Cuban leader José Martí with President McKinley. They are trying to negotiate Puerto Rico's and Cuba's independence with Spain and reach an accord."

"Luis Muñoz Rivera is opening the dialogue with Spain regarding Puerto Rico's autonomy. I hear discussions are progressing," said Manuel. "We can only hope that we reach a proactive resolution, sooner than later. If we achieve autonomy, I wish to preserve a good relationship with Spain. Most of my sales are in Europe, as you know. I must protect the relationship."

"Much is as stake," said Carmona.

41

. . .

Spain finally came through. On November of 1897, the Crown agreed to grant Puerto Rico its independence through the *Carta Autonómica* accord.

"Some great news about the *Carta Autonómica*, would you agree?" said *Alcalde* Carmona at the town meeting.

"I am unsure," Manuel said. "It is good news, but I will be convinced when we hold elections for a new Puerto Rican government, which will not take place until March of next year."

Carmona listened.

"Transitions bring vulnerability," Manuel continued. "Tensions between the United States and Spain have been festering for some time now. I pray nothing happens between now and next March that sets back the process for autonomy for our island."

"But Manuel, one has to have faith!" Carmona said.

"Yes, but I remain skeptical. One thing is not clear to me. What is the United States' incentive to let go of both Cuba and Puerto Rico, when they can try to secure these islands as its territories?" Manuel said. "You have to think strategically. Why would they pass on the opportunity to have land ownership in the Atlantic?"

"What do you mean?" said the mayor. "Puerto Rico has gained its independence from Spain. Are you saying that the United States will just take the country by force?" Carmona said.

"Anything is possible. There is still time, the new government has not been installed, and the United States government knows the island is in a precarious condition. We are still in transition. I just have a suspicion, that is all," said Manuel.

The book written by naval intelligence officer Alfred T. Mahan in 1890, *The Influence of Sea Power Upon History, 1660-1783*, drove United States policy. This book advocated for the United States to take the Caribbean Islands, Hawaii, and the Philippine Islands to establish naval supremacy and bases to protect United States commerce. It also advocated the building of the Panama Canal to facilitate interoceanic transportation. Mahan became the military advisor to President William McKinley.

While the United States had been developing its naval dominance strategy for Latin America for years, it was not until early 1898 that the United States began actual naval preparations to implement its plan against Spain. Mahan's ideas had great influence in this decision, but the media also had a dramatic impact on United States public opinion favoring the war.

"The United States media is advocating for the country to go to battle with Spain and take over Cuba and Puerto Rico to gain advantage over the Atlantic," said Manuel. "They have swayed public opinion. I would not be surprised that the countries go into war, and we are caught in the middle."

Manuel's forecast was accurate. The Spanish-American War is often referred to as "the first media war," because it was in great measure incited by newspapers. William Randolph Hearst, the wealthy and powerful owner and editor of the *New York Journal*, knew that the war would sell his papers and propel him into a national position of prominence. His reporters assigned to Cuba wrote cover stories describing events that would touch the readers' hearts and persuade them to demand United States intervention. Narratives about executions, female imprisonment, the persistent fight by brave rebels, disease and starvation peppered the front pages of Hearst's newspapers. And then came the stories about the sinking of the *USS Maine* battleship in Havana Harbor, unequivocally blaming the Spanish, although to this day there is no proof that Spain caused the explosion onboard.

. . .

"*¡Hundieron el Maine!*" said Manuel to his wife Etervina, as he read the newspaper on February 16, 1898. "They sank the *Maine!*"

"Who? What?" asked the gentle brunette, halting her knitting at the sound of the news.

"It says here that Spain sank the *USS Maine*, the American battleship!" he answered. "*¡Ay Madre! ¡La que se va a formar!* Oh, Mother! Something big is going to happen!"

"But read it to me out loud! What does it say, Manuel?"

"It says that the United States had sent the *USS Maine* battleship to Cuba to protect the United States interests during the Cuban fight for independence against Spain. It says that there was a 'mysterious explosion' of the battleship in the Havana harbor last night, killing 266 men onboard," said Manuel.

"Oh, dear!" she said. "Two-hundred-and-sixty-six lives!"

The explosion became the turning point for the United States to declare war against Spain on April 21, 1898.

United States troops would successively occupy Manila, Cuba and Puerto Rico.

. . .

"I am going to meet with Carmona," said Manuel to his wife. "He has called a town meeting. The Spanish government is organizing volunteer troops. There are news reports that the United States plans to occupy both Cuba and Puerto Rico. I may have to bring the boys along."

"Oh, Manuel!" Etervina said, clutching onto his arm. "I am scared!"

Manuel held Etervina and kissed her gently on her forehead.

"Yes. This is serious," he said. "I will let you all know what transpires."

Alcalde José de la Rosa Carmona communicated to the Spanish military that he had enlisted a local group of volunteers to support the Crown by creating a *Guerrilla Volante Montada* (mounted guerrilla). The Comerío men were ready and willing to fight. Similar volunteer efforts were displayed across the island.

Spain authorized Manuel Fernández Juncos, Puerto Rico's Treasurer, to apply one million *pesos* to the defense of Puerto Rico. Altogether, there were about 18,000 soldiers from which about 8,000 were veterans. The Spanish troops organized into six battalions of about 800 soldiers each, one of which was the *Tiradores de Puerto Rico*, based in San Juan. The volunteer troops organized into 14 battalions with about 6,000 soldiers. There were also about six *guerrillas mixtas* (mixed guerrillas) with about 100 soldiers each, and other forces in each town, including the *guerrillas montadas* (mounted guerrillas). The Spanish naval forces had about six vessels, including the prized Spanish destroyer *Terror*. The walls of the Castles of *San Felipe del Morro* and *San Cristóbal* protected San Juan, with General Ángel Rivero Méndez at the head of artillery at the *San Cristóbal*. They were joined by about 10 other forts and structures peppered throughout the region, armed with cannons and other artillery.

. . .

As part of *The Puerto Rico Campaign*, which began on May 12, 1898, United States forces fired at *El Castillo de San Felipe del Morro (El Morro Castle)* and other fortification structures located in the capital of San Juan and planned a land invasion at some other points in the island, including the town of Fajardo.

On May 12, 1898, Luis Muñoz Rivera, Chief of Government in San Juan, sent a telegram to all town mayors in the island:

"Since dawn, eleven enemy vessels are attacking this city. We are returning fire vigorously. Troops and civilian spirits are high. The bombs are causing little damage. There are some wounded. We believe our artillery is causing damage to the Yankee fleet. They are retreating and have suspended fire. Keep calm and increase exterior surveillance, and promote valor and patriotism of our country. — LUIS MUÑOZ RIVERA."

United States attacks continued in the port of San Juan with plans for bombardments in Arecibo and Fajardo, including positioning to sever underwater telegraph cables as needed to disrupt communications. United States troops of 15,000 strong were prepared to debark at various points in the island.

On July 25, 1898, 3,300 troops set foot in the southern town of *Guánica* and proceeded to *Coamo* at the direction of General Nelson A. Miles, who had changed his strategy at the last minute, surprising both the Spanish military and the United States Department of War. He telegraphed the Department of War three days after his disembarking in Guánica about his change in course:

"Spanish troops are retreating from southern part of Puerto Rico. This is a prosperous and beautiful country. The Army will soon be in mountain region. Weather delightful; troops in the best of health and spirit. Anticipate no insurmountable obstacles in future results. Results thus far have been accomplished without loss of a single life."

At first, the local troops were strong in their will to fight the United States occupation, but a series of unfortunate losses, including the destruction of the Spanish fleet in the Philippines, the loss of the Spanish destroyer *Terror* from the attack by the *USS St. Paul* in the port of San Juan, the loss of the Spanish fleet in Santiago de Cuba, the burning of the *Antonio López* steam cargo ship, and the United States invasion of *Guánica* and *Coamo* weakened the Spanish military's will. In many towns, the locals received the United States troops with open arms, seeing them as their saviors. This was not so in other regions.

Overall, the United States occupation was a rampant success, even though many troops faced difficulty with the island's weather and tropical diseases. One of the soldiers in this group was William Leslie Edison, the son of the famous inventor Thomas Alva Edison, who was stationed in the town of *Coamo* and could not wait to return to the United States due to illness.

. . .

"It's over," said Carmona to the town's men at the *casa alcaldía* (city hall). "Word is that the United States Flag is waving in *Guánica*, *Coamo* and at *El Morro* and *San Cristóbal Castles* in San Juan. Puerto Rico is now United States territory."

"Another transition!" Manuel sighed. "What will this bring?"

On August 13, 1898 Spain agreed to sign a peace accord. On September 4, 1898, Puerto Rican leader Luis Muñoz Rivera gave an interview to *The Chicago Tribune* stating that the proper relationship with the United States for Puerto Rico would be that of becoming a state. The island did not want to continue being a colony.

The last of Spanish troops left Puerto Rico in October of 1898, and the United States established a military government under the command of Major General John R. Brooke. On December 10, 1898, the *Treaty of Paris* was signed, ending the Spanish-American War, resulting in Spain losing its remaining empire in the New World. As part of the deal, Spain transferred Puerto Rico and Guam to the United States at no cost, agreed to receive $20 million for the Philippines, and Cuba obtained its independence.

. . .

On April 12, 1900, the United States Congress enacted the *Foraker Law*, establishing a United States civilian government in Puerto Rico. President McKinley appointed Charles H. Allen as the first governor of the island. Allen had served as Assistant Secretary of the Navy under McKinley.

Some officers within the United States military were not pleased with the appointment of Allen and preferred a stronger leader for the island. In a personal letter to General Robert P. Kennedy on May 2, 1901, William A. Glassford, then major Signal Corps of the United States War Department, expressed that he preferred Kennedy to Allen for the role of governor of Puerto Rico because of Kennedy's prior appointment there. In 1899, President McKinley had appointed Kennedy as President of the Insular Commission directed to investigate and report conditions in Cuba and Puerto Rico, and as such, Kennedy developed knowledge of the island and its people that, in Glassford's opinion, Allen did not possess.

In his letter to Kennedy, Glassford confessed his racial bias against the Puerto Rican people and stated that governing the island would not be as easy as some thought, that a stronger leader was needed for the task.

"Most people go down there thinking that mixture of Indian, Negro and Mediterranean riffraff is favorable to the Anglo-Saxon, and of course is mistaken, for in truth the racial antipathies are not to be crushed out among uncivilized people except in a way so gradual that it need not be considered as prospective," stated Glassford to Kennedy.

The transition from a Spanish to a United States government introduced new economic, cultural, religious and political influences and processes that impacted the culture and way of life in Puerto Rico. It brought some people with narrow mindsets to the island, like Glassford, who thought of the locals as "riffraff," a lesser race. But it also brought educated proactive thinkers, such as Puerto Rico's Commissioner of Education, Dr. Martin G. Brumbaugh.

During his tenure from 1900 to 1902, Brumbaugh immersed himself in the island's people, learned to know them, and genuinely embraced their potential as human beings. In addition to his many achievements, Dr. Brumbaugh, a Pennsylvania Republican born in 1862, had been raised on a farm and understood well the nature of the rural people. He had the difficult task of transitioning Puerto Rico's then-Spanish education system, which was tied to the Roman Catholic Church, to an American-based education system where teachers were laypersons. He created a system of scholarships for students to study abroad in the United States, trained Puerto Rican teachers in the American system, started agricultural trade schools, and ultimately adopted a policy of teaching students in both the Spanish and English languages at all levels. He also started the high-school system, a business school, and the preparatory course required for student entry in United States universities. Besides opening various new schools throughout the island, he installed the Department of Education in San Juan. To date, there are two schools in Puerto Rico bearing his name, one in San Juan and a second in Santa Isabel.

In addition to the many infrastructure changes, the transition to a United States-based rule lifted entry barriers for United States businesses, investors, and Protestant churches. Their leaders had been salivating over the Puerto Rico market of resources and souls well before the small island became a United States territory.

There were grave concerns among Puerto Rican leaders about the manner in which Puerto Rico became a territory of the United States. Many Puerto Ricans worried about the impact the change to a United States government system would have on the four-centuries-old local culture and religion, since the country's roots were still entwined with the Spanish motherland. Much alarm revolved around how the United States, a nation that preached democracy, could use force to take a small country that had just acquired its own democratic self-government and independence from Spain and was en route to implementing its new awaited freedom on its own terms.

Many advocated against the United States' justification for the taking of Puerto Rico. The United States' government position, along with its religious and industrial supporters, was that the American nation was saving Puerto Rico's economy, the lives of its people, and that it was even rescuing its souls by evangelizing the islanders away from Catholicism into the true Protestant faith.

Nevertheless, the political arguments opposing the United States colonization of the small country seemed crushed by the overarching need of the island's poor for food, jobs and medical attention. Spain had left Puerto Rico in terrible disrepair, and the scars of this abandonment showed to a greater degree in the rural zones.

Most poor welcomed the new government's undertakings with open arms, even if these came at the expense of the country's culture and faith. Still, for some local leaders, the United States' strategy was a drug that numbed the minds and the will of many Puerto Ricans who once strived to attain their autonomy from Spain and succeeded, even if for a short time.

For others, who traded the ideals of independence for a more pragmatic solution to the impending poverty, disease and employment needs in the island, if Puerto Rico was not meant to be an independent country, then it deserved the dignity of becoming a state of the United States. It deserved a future away from being a colony. It deserved an identity.

In the midst of each and every argument regarding the status of Puerto Rico, a clear benefit of the transition was clear: The island was now included in the commercial framework of the United States, expanding opportunities for tobacco farmers there and providing tariff protection for Puerto Rican tobacco. Now part of a tax-free export framework, tobacco farming became a key, if not the most important, commercial crop in Puerto Rico.

And this tax incentive favored Manuel Pontón's tobacco business.

The amount of tobacco planted in Puerto Rico tripled from 1897 to 1909. The small island produced about 35 tons of tobacco per year from 1900 to 1927.

Chapter 9. The Tobacco Network

Although the Hurricane *San Ciriaco* of 1899 swept away homes, drowned thousands of souls and decimated entire coffee plantations across the island, the tobacco industry was able to recover quicker than any other from the strong hit. In fact, with the United States tariff incentives introduced after the occupation of the island, the investment in this sector increased, particularly from *Peninsulares* (Spaniards) and descendants of early settlers living in the towns of Comerío, Corozal and Bayamón.

Manuel Pontón continued to build relationships at every level, not only with colleagues, but also with customers, prospects and workers. He was set on the need to integrate with the laborers, as well as the "influentials," as part of his strategy to succeed. Manuel's network with other *Peninsulares* and their descendants included those in Comerío and neighboring towns, such as the *Cobián, Valiente, Longo* and *Martinó* families, also from Infiesto; the *Umpierre* family, whose ancestors emigrated from the Canary Islands; and the *Carmona* family, whose ancestors were said to be early migrants to Puerto Rico from Seville. These families were all involved in agriculture and leveraged their knowledge and relationships with each other in Puerto Rico, and when possible, with their families back in the Spanish mainland.

The quality and productivity of Comerío's tobacco gained recognition with the help of Manuel and other local *industriales*. Award-winning Comerío cigars received a gold medal at an exposition in New York City in 1901. In the early 20th century the town already had three cigar factories: *Cobián y Compañía, La Comerieña,* owned by *Sánchez and Compañía,* and *El Privilegio,* owned by *Santiago Umpierre y Compañía,* the latter being the largest in sales, as well as labor force.

After partnering with *Manuel Valiente y Compañía,* a powerful company based in the neighboring town of Corozal, in 1902 Manuel also became a commissioned agent of *Manuel Pérez y Compañía*, a business based in the neighboring town of Bayamón. This arrangement enabled Manuel Pontón to be "the tobacco broker" for the towns' planters. He also sold the tobacco harvested from his own farms in the *Piñas, Doña Elena, Paloma* and *Cedrito* sectors in Comerío. In addition to these responsibilities, Manuel contracted to care for third-party plantations, and for the collection, conditioning, classification and packaging of tobacco there. Further, his network also offered planters business financing.

Manuel had acquired a key competitive advantage: He was not only a product supplier; he was also the product broker and one of the "venture capitalists" or financiers for the other planters.

Some of Manuel's associates were also his *compadres* (they were baptism godparents to Manuel's children, and vice versa.) For example, Manuel Valiente was the *padrino de bautizo* (baptism godparent) of Sixto, Manuel's third son. The Count of Laviana, Alejandro Villar, was the *padrino de bautizo* of Manolo, Manuel's first son, as well as of some of Manuel's half-siblings in the town of Bayamón.

The Pontón family extended beyond the towns of Comerío and Bayamón. In 1879, José Pontón González traveled from Piloña, Asturias to the town of Fajardo, Puerto Rico as part of the Spanish military, and later settled in Ponce, married Juana Rodríguez Vázquez, and raised a large family. Like Manuel, José was loved in his community. He donated the land for the local school, which still carries his name. There were Asturian Pontóns who also lived in the island of Cuba. Some traveled back and forth across the Atlantic, becoming part of the group of Asturian *Indianos*. Some traveled often to New York. Other Pontóns traveled from Cuba to Florida and established businesses in Tampa's cigar haven, Ybor City in Hillsborough County. Yet there were other Pontóns who traveled from Asturias to Mexico and Peru.

. . .

Thirty years after his arrival in Puerto Rico, Manuel Pontón Fernández was part of one of the most robust tobacco business networks on the island. By the turn of the century, not only had he

51

become a prominent *industrial* in Comerío, he was also a key contributor to the growth of other businesses and his community. Manuel served as the town's *Juez Municipal Suplente* (Substitute Municipal Judge) and councilman, and he consistently paid taxes and participated and voted in the town's elections.

Manuel was also a man of faith, holding strong connections with the Roman Catholic Church, which supported him in the darkest of times.

Chapter 10. Manuel's Religion

The Roman Catholic Church had a long-established power of influence in Puerto Rico and the other Spanish colonies since Columbian times. Under Spanish law, each town was to have a central plaza, where both the church and the *Casa del Rey* ("The King's House" or city hall) were located, facing each other at opposite ends of the square. Catholic priests occupied a high social position in the island for about four centuries, but this began to change with the advent of many Protestant churches of diverse denominations after Puerto Rico became a United States territory.

In 1905, there were 88 Roman Catholic parishes in the island and 120 priests, with about 23 of them in the area of San Juan. There were also various Catholic schools, convents, asylums, orphanages, and missions offering nursing home care, medical services, and care for the poor. Prior to the United States occupation, the only Protestant church in Puerto Rico was an *Episcopal* church in Ponce, which had been established for about 20 years. The church expanded to San Juan and three other towns after 1898. By 1899, the *Methodists* had about 80 congregations in Puerto Rico with 13 missionaries and 18 preachers, and the *Baptists* already had missions in 25 towns in the island. The *Presbyterians* began erecting church buildings right after the occupation and had 66 buildings and five schools in the larger towns. They also built a large hospital in Santurce. The *Adventists* entered in Mayagüez in 1903, the *Christian Alliance* established a mission in Manatí, the *Christian Church* had a mission in Ponce and Salinas, the *Church of Christ* had a mission and an orphanage in Bayamón, and the *Church of Jesus* had a mission and an orphanage in *Quebrada Limón*. The *Congregational Church* had a mission in Fajardo and a mission school in Santurce, the *Lutherans* had a mission in San Juan and a church in Cataño, and the *United Brethren in Christ* had missions in Ponce and Juana Díaz.

53

. . .

The first Roman Catholic parish in Comerío was *Santo Cristo de la Salud* (Holy Christ of Health) and still remains as such. The original church structure, where Father Amador Bisbal married Manuel Pontón and his wife Etervina and later baptized their son José Antonio on September 15, 1883, was built in 1829, not long after the town was founded. It has been remodeled since, but the original building still stands.

Even after the incoming Protestant churches settled in Puerto Rico, Manuel Pontón remained a devout Catholic. He confided in Father Andrés Echevarría, a prominent priest from the *Congregación del Espíritu Santo* (Holy Spirit Congregation) in the neighboring town of Cayey, where Etervina's father grew up. *El Padre Echevarría* was also the Eclesiastical Notary of the Roman Catholic Church in the island of Puerto Rico as of 1905.

Father Echevarría was a conservative, instilling in his followers the importance of abiding by the holy sacraments and engaging in prayer. The priest would provide unwavering strength and support to Manuel during the most trying moments for him and his family.

El Padre Echevarría was ever present for Antonio, until the very end.

Chapter 11. A Privileged Family

When he was around 24 years old, Manuel Pontón Fernández and Josefa Ramos Vázquez had a daughter, María Pontón Ramos (b 1880). Manuel's relationship with Josefa was short-lived. Soon after the birth of María, Manuel married Etervina Elvira Santiago Rivera (b 1863), and they had five children: Manuel (b 1881), José Antonio (b 1882), Etervina (b 1888), Sixto (b 1890) and Mercedes (b 1895).

José Antonio, or Antonio, as they called him at home, was fortunate to have been born into a privileged family. Not only did his father Manuel become a wealthy and influential man, his mother Etervina's family was the cradle to a prominent line of Puerto Rican politicians, intellectuals and leaders. Antonio's second cousin on his mother's side was Luis Muñoz Rivera, founder of the pro-independence movement in Puerto Rico when the island was a Spanish territory. After the United States occupation, Muñoz Rivera became Puerto Rico's first Resident Commissioner to the United States Congress, the island's first delegate to the United States House of Representatives and the force behind the grant of United States citizenship to Puerto Ricans.

Muñoz Rivera, born in 1859 in the town of *Barranquitas*, was the son of Etervina's aunt on her mother's side, Monserrate Rivera Vázquez, and of Luis Muñoz Barrios, a Puerto Rican politician whose father, Luis Muñoz Iglesias, was a Spaniard who fought in the Peninsular War against the Napoleon Bonaparte invasion of Spain in 1808, later migrating to Puerto Rico. Luis Muñoz Rivera's son Luis Muñoz Marín became the first elected governor of Puerto Rico in 1948, under the Popular Democratic Party.

In addition, Antonio and his brothers, particularly Manuel Jr. (Manolo), had a close family relationship with cousin Manuel Tirado Pontón (b 1890), the son of María Pontón Marrero (b 1875) and

Manuel Tirado Rodríguez (b ~1870). María Pontón was Manuel Pontón Fernández's half-sister, born in the neighboring town of Bayamón from the union between Manuel Pontón's father José Pontón Figaredo (b ~1830) and María de los Angeles Marrero (b ~1852). Through the Tirado family, Antonio knew the Barbosa family, also from Bayamón. José Celso Barbosa Alcalá, one of the most admired leaders in Puerto Rican history, was part of this family.

Dr. José Celso Barbosa Alcalá, born in 1857 in Bayamón, was almost the same age as Antonio's father Manuel. A physician and graduate of the University of Michigan medical school, he was a renowned leader and the founder the pro-statehood movement of Puerto Rico. Dr. Barbosa was also a *mulatto* who lost his mother María del Carmen Alcalá Román (b ~1823) when he was only 10 years old. She was a white Venezuelan who migrated to Puerto Rico with her sister Lucía and their mother Eugenia as a result of that country's war of independence.

Hermógenes Barbosa Tirado (b ~1825), Dr. Barbosa's father, was also a *mulatto*, an expert carpenter and master mason with a coveted specialty in building chimneys. He welcomed the help of his young son's aunt Lucía Alcalá Román (b ~ 1815) and her husband Juan José Tirado Rivera (b ~1808) in raising his young child. Juan Tirado was also the brother of the boy's grandmother, Rita Tirado Rivera (b ~1800).

Dr. Barbosa's early education included tutoring in English, enrolling as the only black child in *El Seminario Conciliar de Puerto Rico*, the renowned Catholic school in the island, and later on attending University of Michigan Medical School, where he attained the highest grade of his class. The young boy, through his uncle Juan Tirado, also frequented *El Maestro* Rafael Cordero, an educator of African descent who taught children regardless of their race and social means. *El Maestro Cordero* was known as "The Father of Public Education" in Puerto Rico. Among his pupils were Román Baldorioty de Castro, Alejandro Tápia Rivera and José Julián Acosta, who would all become influential Puerto Rican leaders. *Mamá Lucía* and *Tío Juan* (uncle Juan) did a remarkable job with their nephew, as against all odds he overcame many social and racial barriers to become one of the most endeared *próceres* (leaders) in Puerto Rico. Dr. Barbosa founded the bilingual newspaper *El Tiempo* in 1907, which would help Antonio Pontón when he needed it most.

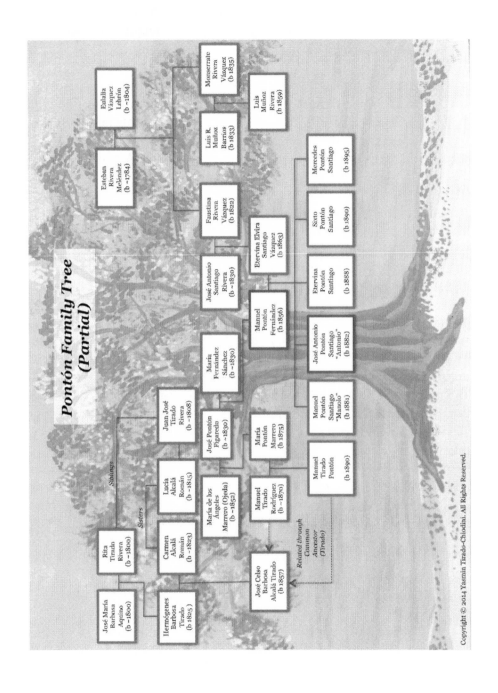

*Pontón Family Tree
(Partial)*

All in all, Antonio grew up a "well-off" child, surrounded by excellent role models and the wealth and influence of self-made *industriales*, educated leaders and politicians. Surrounded by all the ingredients for success, it seemed that he had taken this privilege for granted. A prevailing sentiment in town was that Antonio was careless and spoiled and did not grasp the value of the gift Manuel and Etervina passed on to him.

But ailments were also handed down to Antonio.

. . .

Antonio was a *viva la vida* (local term for those who live to enjoy life with not much accountability.) The ladies ... he enjoyed them too much. "*¡Ay, las faldas!*" ("Oh, the skirts!") he sighed, shaking his head and winking with a mischievous smile. While admitting women were his "Achilles heel," Antonio, as many young men of the times did, also disclaimed responsibility, as though he had no control over his behavior or desires. Loving the opposite sex was "the natural thing to do for a man," he thought. Unlike his father Manuel at his age, Antonio lacked maturity. And although he tried to project a confident image, often succeeding, he was not at peace with himself.

In 1902, when Antonio was 19, he married a young woman from Comerío, Celia Umpierre Carmona, a descendant of the first mayor of Comerío, José de la Rosa Carmona. Everyone wondered if this was a marriage "of convenience," as many other marriages were back then. Families often inter-married in order to preserve their high social status, and love did not have to be part of the equation.

Antonio and Celia's two children died as babies. It did not take long for Antonio to chase *las faldas* (the skirts) again, and Celia showed him the door. Word was that she later found someone else and moved to New York. Antonio always said Celia "was a good wife" and that he was the one with "the problem." People thought he alluded to his weakness with women. They said he was *engreído* (spoiled) and left it at that.

But perhaps it was not as simple as being overindulged. These things are seldom straightforward.

He was a "scatterbrain," a forgetful individual who sometimes searched for his hat when it was already sitting on his own head. Antonio also suffered from severe headaches that disabled him with frequency. These were left unattended, attributed to his temperament as an "attention-grabber." People in town said he was just "overprotected" and "needy." He was often disconnected, lost in his own world, and sometimes he argued with his family and others over the most menial things.

"*Hoy estoy cansado*. Today I am tired," he announced. "I am staying in bed." It was not unusual for Antonio to spend days in his room, excusing himself due to "exhaustion."

But no one could explain why he was so drained when he had not done much of anything. The town's doctor examined him, but he was not anemic and did not show any other physical ailment that may cause him to be lethargic.

Other times, Antonio displayed much energy and appeared to be ready to conquer the world. And for some time, he did. He spent days on the field helping his father oversee the workers, and for the most part, it went well.

Antonio often returned home from the field with a bunch of tobacco flowers for his mother Etervina, as he did when he was a child.

"Here you go *Mamá*," Antonio said. "I brought you some of the pink and white flowers you like."

"*¡Son hermosas!*" she would say about the simple pretty flowers, placing them in a porcelain vase. "Thank you, son. They are beautiful!"

Their aroma never got old.

. . .

On occasion, Antonio would meander and tell jokes to the workers. He had a way to make them laugh.

"One day *Pepito* told his sister she was ugly, and his mother got mad at him," Antonio began telling his *chistes* (jokes) as soon as he arrived at the field.

"Is that so, *Señor* Antonio?" responded a worker with half a smile, as he continued to de-weed the tobacco field. "So, what happened?"

"His mother told him to go back to his sister and say he was sorry."

"So, did he say he was sorry?" asked the worker.

"Yes. He said 'I am sorry you are so ugly, sister'!" said Antonio, as he burst into laughter.

"*¡Ay, Señor Antonio!*" said the worker. "You are going to have to do much better than that. Your *chistes* are getting worse by the day!"

"Antonio!" Manuel had just arrived on his horse. "If you are at the field you better get your hands into the soil and work, or do something productive! Don't go bothering the workers! They need to get their work done. There is no time for distractions!"

"*¡Bueno, padre!* Fine, father!" Antonio said, winking at the workers. And after about an hour of work, he would return home, his face red, sweating rivers.

"*¡Este trabajo es para otro, no para mí!* This work is for someone else, not for me! I just can't bring myself to do it. I am too weak for this type of work. It's so hot, and the tobacco leaves' sap burns my skin and makes me dizzy," Antonio said. "I need to study or do something else. I was not made to work in the field. I am just not built for it!"

As the cycle repeated, Antonio's family endured the ups and downs with him, as passengers in a ship tossed by a tempest; like Manuel's journey as a boy on the *Principe Alfonso* on its way from Asturias to Puerto Rico, only worse.

Despite his immaturity and ailments, Antonio had great potential. Besides being handsome, he was educated, well-spoken, and on his better days, he had the most charming personality. It is possible that these natural qualities, plus his comfortable upbringing and his family's influence and position in the community masked Antonio's vulnerabilities in people's minds. Or maybe folks looked the other way, not wanting any trouble with him or his prominent family.

. . .

While Antonio appeared to be "the carefree spirit" among his siblings, his younger brother Sixto was his opposite. A blond, brown-eyed, strong and decisive young man, Sixto was the most serious and responsible one among the boys. He was a natural businessman, as his father, also bound to be a planter. He became Manuel's right-hand man. Sixto married only once, to María Cristina Carmona Rivera, a relative of Comerío's Mayor during the Spanish-American War, *Alcalde* José de la Rosa Carmona. She was the cousin of Antonio's ex-wife, Celia. By 1911 Sixto and María Cristina had their first daughter, María Isabel. They would have two more daughters, Eva Etervina and Blanca Cristina.

Antonio's older brother Manolo, a green-eyed brunette, heavyset and middle-statured, was skilled in the business of farming and was also driven to become a planter as was his father Manuel. His life goal was simple: to work hard and retire early. By 1905, he had married and divorced beautiful Rosalía Sánchez Ocaña, whose appearance was something out of Harper's Bazaar, with her brown eyes and bobbed onyx hair and the fairest skin, a lover of fashion and the high-end lifestyle. She did well with the divorce settlement, moved to San Juan and used part of the money for cruising to Venezuela and Cuba. They had no children, although their marriage lasted three years. By 1911, Manolo had a second wife, Josefa Rivera Rivera, also the child of a Spaniard. They lived downtown Comerío in *Calle Progreso*. He would have four children with Josefa: another Manuel (blue-eyed *Manolín*) followed by José Osvaldo, Armando and Carmen Rafaela. After Josefa passed of *septicemia* (a bacterial infection of the blood) in 1918, Manolo would father two more daughters: María, from his union with María Pérez de Jesús, and Pilar from his marriage with the daughter of Italian immigrants, Juana Martorani Taranto.

. . .

Antonio's will was different from the will of his two brothers, Sixto and Manolo. A visit to the *Manicomio Insular* (insane asylum) for Antonio was far from consideration, even though some of his mother's relatives had long become acquainted with the institution. Those with melancholy, manic-depressive illness, and other mental ailments could end up there, but not Antonio. He was just *particular*, not depressed. And he was certainly not crazy. He did not belong with *los locos*.

The family would handle his eccentricities in private.

But there was more to Antonio's behavior than many perceived but did not care to uncover. There was a reason why he felt he "could not harmonize" with his family and others, as he once put it.

As Antonio continued his erring ways, Manuel and Etervina resolved to get their son examined by another doctor, a physician in Bayamón, who certified that Antonio did appear to show signs of the family curse. He offered to treat him in private, and they agreed.

But his ailments went beyond heredity.

Passion placed a greater curse on Antonio's will than they ever suspected.

Chapter 12. Freemasonry

In 1910, Manuel and his sons Sixto and Manolo became *Masones* (Freemasons), following in the footsteps of the island's "influentials" of the times. The Masons vowed to support social, cultural, economic and political causes to further their communities. They also committed to accept all religions and races in their membership. These tenets were contrary to ubiquitous conspiracy theories, some of them proposing that Masons were set to overthrow governments, had anti-Christian beliefs and worshipped the devil. Some linked Masons to *The Knights Templar* and the *Illuminati*, and they were alleged to have the ultimate objective of attaining world control.

In fact, many 19th and 20th Century "great thinkers" in Puerto Rico, such as political and social leaders Luis Muñoz Rivera, José Celso Barbosa, José de Diego, Eugenio María de Hostos and Ramón Emeterio Betánces, to name a few, were Freemasons. A number of contemporaneous United States Presidents were also Freemasons, including William McKinley, Theodore Roosevelt, and William Taft.

Regis H. Post, the Governor of Puerto Rico from 1907 to 1909, appointed by President Theodore Roosevelt, was also a Freemason and was present at the 1909 inauguration of the temple of the *Logia Loarina* (Loarina Lodge) #17 in the town of Bayamón, the same lodge attended by Dr. José Celso Barbosa.

Freemasonry arrived in Puerto Rico in the early 19th century, with lodges obtaining warrants from Massachusetts and the Grand Orient of France. Afraid that Masons would impair their government in the colonies, Spain made membership of a masonic order punishable by imprisonment and death. Spain lifted the suppression around 1860. As a result, various lodges established chapters in the island, *The Grand Lodge of Cuba* and the Lodge of *El Grande Oriente Español* being two of them.

Manuel and his sons Sixto and Manolo were members of the Spanish Lodge *Grande Oriente Español*, Chapter *Gloria y Libertad* Number 316 of the Valley of Comerío, Puerto Rico.

Antonio never cared to join.

"All the Masons do is *cacarear* ('jibber jabber') like hens in a pen," said Antonio. "All the ceremonious stuff makes me anxious! The hats! The robes! The tassels! The strange symbols! It's too complicated. I have enough with going to church! That's enough ceremony for me! All this Mason stuff is nonsense! Let me know when women are allowed to attend the meetings, and I may reconsider joining, especially if they are pretty!" he said jokingly.

Manuel did not force his rebellious son to join the civic organization that served him so well with his community work and also with his business. He agreed, the Masons were better off without Antonio, and Antonio was better off without the Masons.

Little did he know!

Chapter 13. The "Don Juan" Syndrome

The popular culture in non-urban areas in Puerto Rico incentivized a man to be a *Don Juan*, a *mujeriego* (womanizer). In some rural communities, it was a symbol of manhood and status for men to have one or more concubines and even procreate with them.

In 1899, about 16.6 percent of the Puerto Rican population was married, 8.8 percent was living together in a consensual union, a large 69.7 percent were children, and around 16 percent of the total population consisted of illegitimate children. Although statistics show there were more males than females in the island at the turn of the century, many males were children, so there were in effect more women than men of marrying age.

Similar to early rural colonial practices in the United States, such as in rural Maryland, some Puerto Ricans resorted to a consensual marriage rather than formalizing their union through civil or religious means. As in the United States, this was not necessarily because people were amoral, but because consensual marriages were customary. For many, from a financial perspective, marriage was a luxury. People in rural communities had to travel long distances in order to legally register a marriage. Some simply did not have the financial resources to pay for the fees of the civil registration, the church donation and the costs of the ceremony. As "common law marriage" became more accepted, some well-off people in rural communities were known to also adopt this practice, only to formalize the relationship years after, if ever.

In addition, the discriminatory laws, religious beliefs, the stressed economy and the customs of the day forced many women to depend on a man to secure their future, whether the man was a father, relative, husband or partner. A woman's property rights were limited, she had few work prospects outside the home, and she could not vote or travel alone. This levied an enormous burden on single women, and in particular, on those of humble means.

To add to the challenges for women, many islanders were succumbing to anemia, tuberculosis, malaria, yellow fever, smallpox, typhoid fever, and other diseases. Those affected were, to a great extent, women in rural areas. The mentality was to ensure the man had someone to take care of his children in the event their mother passed. Therefore, some women would tolerate unconventional relationships, even with married men, for a chance at securing their future. Indeed, there were instances when a man lived with both his wife and his concubine, either next-door or even in the same household, although this was infrequent.

To increase opportunities for women during the turn of the 20th century, some educated and elite women in the island followed the suffragist movement in the United States and worked to raise the bar for women's rights in Puerto Rico. There was also an overt pro-education movement proposing that women "were called on to save society" because as the ones nurturing the children, "they were owed" an opportunity for higher education. Children would benefit from being raised by educated mothers, and this in turn would benefit society. These efforts centered in San Juan and the larger urban clusters in the island.

Nevertheless, although some women began to study to become teachers, many remained uneducated and were reduced to work in *materias de su sexo* (matters pertaining to their sex) depending on a man for survival. An uneducated woman who "did not have a man" would have to find a means to survive through agricultural labor (such as being a *despalilladora* in a tobacco farm), as a seamstress, a cook, a domestic laborer, or assume other acceptable manual tasks.

It was not until 1935 that all women could vote in Puerto Rico. The United States Constitution's 19th Amendment rights to vote were not extended to Puerto Rican women. In 1929, Puerto Rico's Law Number 27 granted voting rights to women over 21 who knew how to read and write. Puerto Rico's Law Number 4, enacted on March 23, 1935, granted voting rights to all women, regardless of their educational status.

The culture of a woman's dependence on a man for survival intertwined with the long-lived tradition where a man must conquer a woman's affections; where a man persisted in the pursuit of a woman, and better one who seemed unattainable. The more difficult the woman was to access, the more virtue she possessed and the more suitable for marriage she would become. Some men stalked women until they gave in, as hunters in pursuit of their prey.

Once the thrill of the chase was over, while some men found monogamous married life suitable, many just could not sustain it; perhaps because they "did not have it in them," or maybe they had not yet found true love, like Antonio.

Part II. Bound for New York

"Give me your tired, your poor,
Your huddled masses, yearning to breath free,
The wretched refuse of your teeming shore,
Send these, the homeless, tempest-tossed to me,
I lift my lamp beside the golden door."

- Emma Lazarus
Segment from inscription in plaque
at the pedestal of the Statue of Liberty

Chapter 14. Adiós

Too many late nights, his drinking, his tempestuous temperament, the countless women, and the babies who came along the way, prompted Manuel and Etervina to help redirect the course of their son's future. Dangerous incidents, such as the one when Antonio drove a passenger-filled car in reverse for miles at high speed on a dare, were too much of a load to bear.

Antonio Pontón was out of control, like his horse when it fell down the cliff. Rumors were that he pushed the animal down to see how its natural instinct would save it, like a twisted scientific experiment.

"I told you it was accident!" Antonio denied the rumors when his parents confronted him. "I could have fallen down the cliff with it had I not jumped off the poor animal when it went crazy!" he insisted. "*¡Les digo que se volvió loco el caballo ése!* That horse went crazy, I tell you!"

He wanted nothing to do with his father's tobacco business, but he performed well in his studies and wanted a profession. Perhaps sending Antonio abroad to study could break the cycle of his disorderly life and "help him mature," the loving parents thought. Antonio's will needed to be tamed. All the nonsense had to end.

Antonio agreed. He needed a change of scenery.

So, Manuel and Etervina resolved to send their son to New York to pursue a career in law at the prestigious Albany Law School, about two hours from New York City.

. . .

On July 8, 1911, days before it was time to start preparing Manuel's land for the tobacco seedbeds, Antonio Pontón left his family and friends behind in Comerío and prepared to embark on his five-day steamboat journey to New York. José Juan, one of Manuel's workers, drove Antonio, Manuel and Etervina to the Port of San Juan. There, the driver unloaded Antonio's trunk, and carried it to be stowed on the ship.

"*Bendición Mamá*," Antonio said to Etervina, following tradition and asking for her blessing, as he prepared to board the *SS Caracas*. "I promise to write often."

Etervina placed both hands on her son's cheeks and caressed his face with her thumbs, looking into his big green eyes. She wept, already hoping for his safe return.

"*Diós te bendiga. Cuídate hijo mío*," insisted Etervina, asking God to bless her son and begging Antonio to take care of himself.

He was the first one in the family to leave the nest. The first one to go to a university.

"*Así lo haré, Madre. No se preocupe. ¡Tranquila!*" said Antonio in Castilian Spanish, still spoken in the island back then, trying to reassure his mother he would do as she asked, not to worry, to calm down.

Etervina opened her purse and pulled out a small black wooden box, which she gave to her son.

When he opened the box, Antonio saw that it contained a gold pocket watch of about two inches in diameter, resting on soft black felt. He removed the watch from its case to admire its detail. It had a beautiful ivory fascia, and its chain was made of an intricate heavy gold. On the reverse of the watch, engraved cursive letters read *Antonio Pontón Santiago*.

Speechless, jewel in hand, Antonio embraced his mother. "*¡Gracias, mi angel!* Thank you, my angel!" he said to Etervina. "It is beautiful! I will always carry it with me, to remind me of you!"

"Farewell my son," said Manuel to Antonio with teary eyes, shaken by his son's departure. "You know what to do!" Manuel issued a direct command to Antonio to behave, looking straight into his eyes.

"Will he settle down and get a hold of his life, once and for all?" Manuel's mind asked. "One could only hope and pray."

Walking towards the *Caracas*, Antonio turned his head slightly to capture a mental image of his parents one last time. In the far distance, he saw a young woman with two little ones about four and two years old standing by her side. The children waved at him.

"*¡Ay, Ay, Ay!*" Antonio sighed.

She made a gesture with her hands, as though saying, "I am sorry. I gave in!"

Indeed, she had succumbed under the spell of the children's repeated requests to take them to the Port of San Juan to say a final farewell to their father. Antonio stared at the children for a minute with both a frown and a smile, and then he signaled at them to come over to him.

The children ran towards their father and launched at him, hugging him, giggling. He returned their embrace and kissed them, picking up the smaller one in his arms.

"*Acordaos de lo que os dije ayer, ¡Portaos bien!*" he reminded them to behave while he was gone, repeating what he had told them the day prior when he visited them to say goodbye. After promising to mail them postcards, the father sent the children back to their mother.

Antonio thought the kids would be better off without him, for the time being. He was just not ready to be a father. He himself needed to sort things out. It was time. And the children had the support of the Pontón family, even if their mother and father were not meant to have a future together.

Obedient, little Antonio and Manolo followed their father's instructions. He watched them skip away, but on the return path to their mother, they sidetracked.

"*¡Abuela! ¡Abuelo!* Grandmother! Grandfather!" screamed little Antonio and Manolo at their grandparents, as they ran with their arms open, ready to hug Manuel and Etervina. They held them in a loving embrace, kissed them and sent them on their way back to their mother.

As the children left, Antonio shifted his gaze towards his father and gently waved at his family, while they returned the gesture.

With half a smile and a tight lip, Antonio's green eyes spoke, "*Adiós*" ("Good-bye").

Then, he turned and walked towards the green metal door of the steam cargo vessel that swallowed him away.

This was the last time they saw Antonio alive.

Chapter 15. Plans and Hopes

Manuel would pay for everything. He wanted to make sure his son Antonio focused all his time and efforts on his studies. He wished for no distractions for his son and often daydreamed of the moment Antonio would return home a lawyer, and along with his brothers Sixto and Manolo, they would manage Manuel's land and his tobacco business. Together, the sons would keep Manuel's legacy alive.

Manuel was so hopeful.

In four years Antonio would finish his studies. The first year, he would master the English language, and then he would course three years of law school. When finished, he would return home for good, a distinguished lawyer and a graduate of the Albany Law School, one of the best academic institutions in the United States.

"He will be back in the blink of an eye," Manuel said, in a failed attempt to lift frail Etervina's spirits. "He'll be fine. You'll see?" he said, almost sounding as though he was asking a question, rather than making a statement.

"*Sí. ¡El tiempo vuela!*" good Etervina replied to her husband, trying to minimize the void left in her heart by her son's absence. "Yes. Time flies!" she said.

She looked at her empty vase, wondering who would bring her tobacco flowers, now.

Chapter 16. El Remolino

Antonio looked forward to his newfound freedom away from home. He had never traveled outside of Puerto Rico before. The trip on the *Caracas* ocean liner from San Juan to New York across the Atlantic was not as rocky as he anticipated from his father's voyage stories, although he was taken by seasickness.

The *SS Caracas* was a cargo liner from the United States' company *Red D Line*, in business since 1839. The ship was manufactured in 1889, weighed about 3,000 tons, and although it was smaller than the large 6,500-ton ocean freighters, it had more passenger room. It could carry about 130 passengers in outside cabins with two or three beds, some of them with berths, private showers, toilets and running water, as well as fans. The *Caracas* also featured a cozy restaurant. The Red D Line promoted the food served in the ship as "splendid, hotel-quality meals." The ship had wide promenades with deck chairs for passengers to sit and relax, read a book, or play a game of shuffleboard. Golf, with tethered golf balls, was also available. A steward was assigned "to the beck and call" of the passengers from dawn to dusk, or later if they wished to stay up in the evenings to enjoy the new lounge and smoking room.

Staying in his cabin was not Antonio's idea of fun, despite the seasickness. He made an effort to compose himself and visit the ship's amenities, smoke a cigar or two, and see if a good cocktail would help him regain his composure, perhaps a cognac. After a couple of days, his body got used to the slight rocking of the *Caracas*.

"This is not as bad as *Padre* forecasted," Antonio thought, recalling Manuel's stories of seasickness during his journey as a boy from Asturias to Puerto Rico on the *Principe Alfonso*. But Antonio's was not the same vessel or circumstances Manuel experienced when he sailed away from his motherland. Not even close.

As the ship approached the Port of New York, the busiest in the world, Antonio became energized.

"What magnificent sights!" he said to the other passengers lined up on the deck.

The *Statue of Liberty* was even more impressive than he had ever imagined, soaring over 300 feet above New York's harbor. Its verdigris color was a couple shades lighter than Antonio's green eyes.

"I had heard about the statue's colossal size, but I never envisioned it to be so majestic in person," he said.

His mind was busy wondering what angle of *Lady Liberty* he admired most. He preferred the front, as it detailed her face and her hand's strong grip of the torch, raised to the heavens by her right arm, as though she was toasting him to his new life. Antonio was drawn to female beauty, but he became mesmerized by women who were also strong and intelligent, like *Lady Liberty*.

Ellis Island, the place of passage for so many immigrants!

The crowd at customs was unbelievable. Antonio observed the majority of the immigrants there were Italian, followed by Polish and Irish. Being a Puerto Rican, Antonio could go through customs as a United States citizen, even though he was not. There was a United States government order to "treat all documented Porto Ricans as United States citizens" for the purposes of customs. Antonio stood in the United States Citizens' line, got his paperwork inspected and stamped, and took the ferry to New York City.

. . .

The skyline of New York! The different structures and architecture, the height of the skyscrapers, the numerous tall buildings, all so close together! The *Singer Building*, the *Met Life Tower*, the *Woolworth Building,* already under construction, its tower projected to be the tallest in the world when its construction concluded.

New York's history permeated the air Antonio breathed. This feeling was diffused only in the presence of a beautiful woman walking by.

"*¡Ave María!*" Antonio found himself mumbling praises to the Virgin Mary at the sight of the beautiful female pedestrians.

His inner voices began to struggle.

"*¡Esto va a ser fenomenal!*" ("This is going to be great!") a voice inside him whispered in excitement.

"¡Ya basta!" ("Stop that, already!") another voice scolded him. *"¡Sabes lo que te ha dicho tu padre!"* ("You know what your father said!")

Antonio listened to the voices, constrained by their conflicting counsel.

Fighting temptation always proved to be an arduous task. Antonio often walked on a tightrope, and he could only hope that there was a protective net below to catch his fall. But there was no net in New York. He was no longer in Comerío, shielded by his father Manuel's discipline and his mother Etervina's love.

Smitten, Antonio was convinced that New York was where he belonged, not in the small town of Comerío, dealing with the hot and humid tropical weather, the tobacco and the farm, struggling to get along with everyone. He should live in a big city such as this one, where he could expand his horizons. Perhaps he could be a business lawyer. This is as close as he could come to working in his father's business.

"Should I become a doctor instead?" he wondered to himself. "Nah!" he discarded the passing thought. "Interesting, but it can get messy."

Antonio thought New York was his long-awaited liberation. But it would be much to the contrary. He would be suctioned into a *remolino,* a merciless whirlpool from which there was no escape.

Chapter 17. Schenectady

Since there was a colony of Puerto Rican students and workers living in Schenectady, New York, about two hours from Albany Law School, Antonio sought to settle close to this town. His initial plan was to find a boarding place and also secure an English language tutor in preparation for law school. He had received a map with travel instructions from fellow Puerto Rican Albany Law School students to guide his travel from New York City to Schenectady via the New York Central Railroad.

Schenectady was part of the Dutch colony of New Netherland. In 1777, during the American Revolutionary War, the 2nd Albany County Militia Regiment, the local militia unit, fought there against the British Loyalist troops during the *Battle of Saratoga*, the turning point in the American Revolution.

Antonio stayed at *The Edison Hotel* on State Street while he searched for a more permanent housing situation.

. . .

"Good afternoon. My name is Mrs. Anna Warner. What brings you to Schenectady?" asked the hotel matron making conversation with Antonio during check-in.

"I jus araiv hear from Puerto Rico," Antonio responded in halting English, thickened by his natural Spanish accent. "I go to Albany Loskool nex yir, but firs I tek Inglich lehson. I luk for a ples while I tek lehson."

"Is it Puerto Rico or Porto Rico?" Mrs. Warner asked.

"It is P-u-e-r-t-o Rico," Antonio responded. "The naym of Porto Rico was mistek on the *Tratado de París*, signed after the American ocupaychon of the iceland. Sins then, Americans say *Porto Rico*, but that's no right. It's P-u-e-r-t-o Rico. Everybohdy have problem wit langhesh! Like me!" he said smiling, acknowledging his own struggle.

The error was corrected in 1932.

"Oh, Mr. Pontón, your English is very good!" she said. "I wish I could speak Spanish the way you speak English. At least I could speak another language!"

"Sankju. I red betteh than I spik. I tek it in hyehskool after the ocupaychon, but nid practis. I wunt to spik perfec for loskool. I herd from other Puerto Rican student that Chohari is a goot ples to stey whail lernin Inglich," Antonio said.

"Yes, you should look at the Village of Schoharie. Some of the residents there rent rooms to students and some students are from Porto Rico. My apologies, Puerto Rico," she said.

"I wil luk. Sankju," he said. "Are ju from Chenectady, Meeses Guahrner?"

"I have never left Schenectady ever since I was born!" said Mrs. Warner with a smile. "I would love to see Puerto Rico. People say it is a tropical paradise!"

"I never liv Puerto Rico befor also," said Antonio. "But my father Manuel Pontón is from Spain. He travel to Puerto Rico when child. Jehs, Puerto Rico is beeuhteefool! Ju chood visit some time, if ju can!"

"Here you go, you may want to read this so you can become familiar with Schenectady," Mrs. Warner said to Antonio as she lent him a book from the hotel's library.

"Sankju," he said. "I rid it. The name Chenectady is hard to sey for me."

"The name of the town is a *Mohawk Indian* name which means 'near the pinery,'" said Warner. "It is difficult to pronounce, but I am sure you'll get used to saying it, especially since you will be living here at least through law school!"

"Interestin. My toun Comerío is also indian naym. A Taeeno Indian naym of a cheef," said Antonio. "What coeensidens!"

"It certainly is!" said Mrs. Warner. "There is quite a bit of Indian influence in our culture."

"Many Puerto Rican moov to Chenectady to estohdy and wok," said Antonio to Mrs. Warner.

"This is true, many immigrants are coming to New York. To tell you the truth, it is somewhat intimidating for some of the locals, but when it is good for business, I cannot complain!" said Mrs. Warner.

In 1880, Schenectady was still a small town with about 15,000 residents spread within about 11 square miles. The Erie Canal and railroads gradually injected commerce to Schenectady. In 1887, the inventor Thomas Alva Edison moved his company *Edison Machine Works* to Schenectady, and in 1892 the town became the headquarters of the *General Electric Company* (the former Edison Machine Works). The business was a major economic influence along with the *American Locomotive Company* (ALCO), and this helped establish the city and region as a manufacturing center, earning it the nickname of "Electric City."

The increased demand for employees drew an influx of people to Schenectady. The town grew from about 31,682 residents in 1900 to 72,826 by 1910. At the end of the 19th century, Schenectady had a large population of Polish and Italian residents. There was also a colony of Puerto Ricans drawn to the area seeking higher education and employment opportunities, most of the growth spur triggered by the Spanish-American War of 1898.

"Albany Law School is part of Union College, the oldest college campus in the United States," said Mrs. Warner. "It was established in 1795, a great school."

"I kno it's a goot eskool," said Antonio. "Some friend I kno went to Albany Loskool. This is why I come hear," he said. "They like."

She smiled.

"Do ju hav noospayper Meeses Guahrner?" he asked.

"Yes, we receive the *Schenectady Gazette*," Mrs. Warner said. "You are welcome to read it."

"Sankju, madam," Antonio said.

After check-in, Antonio went to his room to wash up. He read about Schenectady in the book Mrs. Warner gave him, and he also read the newspaper in search of a suitable boarding arrangement. Then he came downstairs for dinner.

"Did you find anything interesting in the newspaper, Mr. Pontón?" Mrs. Warner asked as he walked past the lobby.

"Jehs, I fond a room for rent in Beelach of Chohari. Room and bord for seben dolar a wik."

"That sounds good, Mr. Pontón. I would go see it if I were you," said Mrs. Warner.

"Dhaer is olso Inglich tutor in the house. Perfec for me!" said Antonio.

"Good!" said Mrs. Warner.

Antonio took directions from Mrs. Warner on how to travel to the Village of Schoharie by railroad.

"Bery wel. I go tomoro mornin. Sankju for all jur help!" said Antonio, proceeding to the dining room.

After eating, Antonio retreated to his room for the evening and began writing his first letter to his parents.

Chapter 18. Mi Querida Familia

"*Mi querida familia*" ("My Dear Family"). Antonio's early letters to Comerío described the initial impressions of his trip from San Juan to New York, Schenectady, and the breathless sights on his way to the small town of Schoharie by railroad.

Schoharie was, and still remains, a rural area populated by farms, forests, and rural residences. It sits about 39 miles away from Albany, and 28 miles from downtown Schenectady, with magnificent natural beauty and environmental resources, with numerous springs, caves, sinkholes and cracked limestone pavement peppered throughout the area.

The name "Schoharie" was derived from the Indian word *To-Was-Scho-Hor*, which means "driftwood." Palatine Germans settled the area beginning in 1711. The main farming products there were hops, wheat and corn. The *Village of Schoharie* was incorporated in 1867. The town's population was 2,588 already by 1850. In 1865, the *Albany and Susquehanna Railroad* was built, which passed through Central Bridge, where George Westinghouse, Jr., one of the world's best-known inventors, was born in 1846. There, he founded the *Westinghouse Corporation*, but for business reasons he later moved it to Pittsburgh, Pennsylvania.

. . .

The Kromer house was located on 27 Main Street, within walking distance to the Village of Schoharie, the beautiful historic downtown, and it was also in close proximity to the *Middleburgh and Schoharie Railroad* station on Depot Street. It sat on an attractive green lot, off the road, surrounded by plenty of trees and flowering shrubs. The two-story wooden house was painted white and had a pitched dark gray slate roof, with a red brick chimney. The glass windows were divided in four panes and had black shutters. Four white wooden stairs with flimsy handrails on both sides gave access to the front of the house. They were centered with the main door; their width was about a third of the width of the house. The stairs came up to a small open front porch supported by plain white wooden columns. There were windows, one on each side of the main door. The door was black and had a plain brass knocker and a small square window on the top half, with beveled glass.

Antonio knocked. A middle-aged lady opened the door.

"Good morning," she said.

She was a short blond lady in her fifties with a triangular face, big blue eyes, a small nose and a pointed chin.

"How do ju do, madam? I am hear for the room," Antonio said. "My naym is Antonio Pontón. I hav a letter of aseptens from Albany Loskool and a letter from my father if ju nid to see my documents."

Antonio removed his hat and offered Mrs. Kromer his documents, which she gave a cursory review.

"Very well. Please come in," she said. "I am Mrs. Nora Kromer."

Mrs. Kromer's lips joined in almost a straight line and were thin, almost nonexistent. She was of medium weight. She wore a light blue buttoned-up ankle-length dress with a belt at the waist and three-quarter sleeves.

As soon as he entered the Kromer house, Antonio caught the scent of fresh flowers. He noticed the delicate wallpaper and the mahogany staircase to the second floor on his right. It was a straight line upstairs, with simple balusters.

"These are my daughter and son, Bessie and Charles," Mrs. Kromer said.

Her daughter Bessie and her son Charles, both in their early twenties, joined Mrs. Kromer during the house tour. Bessie was a beautiful brown-eyed young woman. But Antonio knew better than to stare at her in front of her mother.

Mrs. Kromer covered the majority of her hair with a light-colored bonnet trimmed with lace and thin ribbons at the end, used to tie the bonnet under her chin in a simple bow. She seldom smiled and seemed set in her ways, focusing on the task at hand, showing the house to the potential boarder.

"*Por favor, deme su sombrero y chaqueta,*" said Bessie to a surprised Antonio. "Please give me your hat and jacket."

She hung them on the coat rack by the entrance.

"Sankju! Jur Spanish is purfect!" said Antonio with admiration.

"*¡Muchas Gracias!*" Bessie responded, with a shy smile.

Bessie translated for her mother, as she knew some Spanish. She wore her hair in a loose Victorian bun that day. Charles, a tall introverted young man with brown hair and hazel eyes, just followed them around, a shadow, smiling from time to time.

The wooden floors were beautiful, but squeaky. The living room on the left side of the house had a stunning brick mantle and a fireplace. The house had a warm feeling, and it was furnished with beautiful German wooden pieces throughout. There was also an enclosed back porch, Antonio's favorite area already, decorated with plants, some chairs and a small round coffee table. Antonio did not get to see the upstairs because these were dedicated quarters for the Kromer family.

"And here is the room for rent," said Mrs. Kromer.

Antonio's room was on the first floor towards the back of the house, on the right. It had light walls, and it was modest, but clean. A window opposite to the main entrance to the room provided bright light and looked out on a nice medium-sized tree. The room had a single bed with its left side against the wall across from the window. A small oak side table rested next to the bed, against the back wall. The room also had a simple wooden desk and chair by the window. The desk had a couple of drawers on each side.

There was also a small oak *chifferobe* armoire with two side-by-side compartments. On its left side there was just enough room to hold Antonio's pressed suits and shirts and store his shoes. On its right side there was a small mirror at the top, a small jewelry drawer which could be locked with a key, a cabinet for his hats with a door that opened by pulling a brass knob on the left side, and three drawers where he could place his underwear, socks, ties, bowties and handkerchiefs. He could store any other items in his steamer trunk, which doubled as a small armoire, if needed.

All bed dressings and towels were included. A small bathroom was outside the room, towards the back of the house, but it was accessible through a small door by the bed, and he did not have to share it. The bathroom had a small window overlooking the back yard, a small sink, a claw foot bathtub and an oval-shaped mirror. There was a small cabinet for fresh towels and a hook on the wall to hang his towel to dry.

Schoharie was a quiet town, suitable for studying. People seemed friendly. The air was fresh. Antonio was pleased.

"Sankju Meesees Kromer. I will tek the room. Jur haus is beeuhteefool," said Antonio.

Looking at Bessie and smiling, he said, "I also nid Inglich lehson."

Bessie returned the smile.

"Very well," said Mrs. Kromer.

Antonio secured the place with a first-week deposit.

"I wil be hear tomoro," he said.

"It is settled," said Mrs. Kromer.

They walked with him outside the main entrance, where he put his hat and jacket back on.

"Meesees Kromer, Mees Kromer," he said, tipping his hat off while looking at them.

"Meester Kromer," he said. He began to walk away as they closed the door.

The next day, Antonio checked out of The Edison Hotel and moved into the Kromer home.

. . .

A few months after arriving in Schoharie, Antonio relayed some good news to his parents: His English lessons were progressing, and he was becoming fluent in his second language, at least conversationally. His accent was softening, too. He just had to work harder at expanding his vocabulary, and he needed more practice to avoid pronouncing his *y's* like *j's* and his *sh's* like *ch's*. The *ee's* were a definitive challenge for Antonio. He was stuck on pronouncing them as "*eh's*." People were confused when he pronounced "sheep" as "chip," for example. He was improving, but in his mind, he needed to polish these subtleties to succeed in law school.

Antonio noticed that some of the locals were impatient with foreigners. Many of them "avoided the immigrants," as though they did not want "any trouble." He did not want native speakers to think he was dangerous or lacked intelligence because he spoke with an accent. He realized there were issues with some of the immigrants, the Italians, Polish and some of the Irish. This was for the most part in

"The City," but it also permeated through Schoharie. He reasoned it was because "there were too many immigrants," and some went to work and left the older kids at home unsupervised. Some of the kids got in trouble. People were intimidated. Then there were the issues with *the mobsters*.

But not all immigrants were gangsters, much to the contrary. They were just seeking better life. The small town's locals needed to make an effort to understand the different cultures of the immigrants. It was clear that the situation could be handled better if both sides were more open-minded.

"All Americans were immigrants at one point or another," he explained in his letters to his parents.

Even his father Manuel migrated to Puerto Rico. Manuel was deemed a *Peninsular*, an immigrant from Spain, and sometimes even the Puerto Rican-born, the *criollos*, resented the Spanish-born newcomers. Manuel was familiar with being singled out, although not quite as much as Antonio felt while in New York.

"It is amazing how people tend to forget their past," Antonio wrote to his parents, surprised. "I recall what you told me about *Maestro* Rafael, *Papá*, when he said to you '*never forget your history.*'"

"Having an accent is quite appealing to some of the young ladies here," was a thought Antonio would not share with his parents. He resolved to "try to turn it off" just for law school, but not when he was flirting with his female prospects. "It attracts some of the women," he noticed, keeping that treasured finding to himself.

There were only a few more months of English lessons left for Antonio to polish the nuances, expand his vocabulary and begin his coursework at Albany Law School.

"P.S. It is taking me some time to get used to some of the food here. It is too bland. And I don't like cabbage! Cabagge is for horses! I miss your cooking, *Mamá!*" he wrote once, knowing his mother would have a laugh at his remark.

The future was full of promise for Antonio!

. . .

Other letters followed, each bringing to life vivid images of the small town of Schoharie. Antonio described how he admired the Greek

Revival architecture of some of the buildings and old historical landmarks like the *Old Stone Fort* and the *Iron Bridge*. But for some odd reason, perhaps his romantic spirit, he preferred rustic places such as the *Old Blenheim Bridge*, a wooden covered bridge in neighboring Blenheim, not too far away from his new home on 27 Main Street.

Although he had never seen a covered bridge before, the scenery somehow reminded him of *La Represa El Salto*, the dam back in Comerío. It was peaceful there, the structures defied nature, and the river was calm, but grand. As with *La Represa*, Antonio wondered what would happen with the bridge during the rainy season. He recalled that when it rained for days, back in Comerío, the *La Plata River* would grow out of its course, flooding the surroundings. The dam helped, but during storm season the amount and force of the water could be overwhelming. Before the dam was opened, the residents in nearby homes had to be evacuated and relocated to shelters or with family or friends elsewhere, only to come back to what was left of their homes, if anything. Still, they would rebuild, because this was the only land they had. All tobacco planted near the river's bed would be lost. It was a calculated risk they took, which sometimes paid off.

In his letters, Antonio also described his first visit to Saratoga Springs.

"It's called Saratoga Springs because they have thermal springs just as in the *Baños de Coamo*," Antonio wrote, referring to the famous thermal waters in the town of Coamo in Puerto Rico. "They have bath houses where you can swim and relax, like in Coamo," he explained.

He described how Saratoga Springs visitors could drink the water from some of the springs and how its taste was a bit salty, as some springs had a strong mineral concentration.

"The locals say it is good for your health," he wrote to Manuel and Etervina. "Maybe the waters could help me with my headaches."

Coamo is a Taíno word meaning "flat and extended space." According to local legend, the first Spanish governor of Puerto Rico, Juan Ponce de León, heard about the healing powers of the *Baños de Coamo* from the *Taíno* Indians. Believing that the baths were *The Fountain of Youth* he was seeking, Ponce de León asked for its location. However, he misunderstood the instructions given to him by the Indians to "Go west for a long time" and instead of going by land, he headed west by sea, resulting in the discovery of Florida and the eventual death of the famous Spanish conquistador.

The *Baños de Coamo* gained international attention when a Spaniard by the name of Usera Soriano built a resort there in 1857, attracting many notable international visitors, including Franklin D. Roosevelt, Frank Lloyd Wright, Alexander Graham Bell, and Mr. and Mrs. Thomas A. Edison.

After Thomas A. Edison passed away, his letters revealed that his son, William Leslie Edison, about five years older than Antonio, quit Yale College in New Haven Connecticut due to poor grades. He enlisted in the United States Army's First New York Regiment of Volunteer Engineers during the Spanish-American War of 1898 and was stationed in Coamo. William's letters to his father indicated that he was not tolerant of the Puerto Rican weather whatsoever and pleaded with his father to use his influence to have him moved out of the island, suggesting he would die of malaria otherwise.

However, it seems Mr. Edison could not pull any strings to transfer his son away from Puerto Rico. While William was there during the war, one of the structures built in the *Baños de Coamo* was destroyed by United States artillery. This location was later rebuilt and visited by the notables mentioned. After his return from the military, William continued to face obstacles with his health, which he attributed to "the business of Porto Rico," and was often dependent on his father.

Antonio told Manuel and Etervina that he was disappointed that the horseracing course was closed when he went to Saratoga Springs, due to New York's anti-gambling legislation. He would have enjoyed betting on a horse so much more than betting on a rooster, as people did back in Comerío. And although the traditional *peleas de gallos* (cockfights) back home were exciting to men there, Antonio thought that horseracing was a much classier sport.

"You could make a nice day of visiting the horseracing course, dressed up in your finest clothes," he wrote home. "Although you are still betting on an animal's performance, watching horses race one another is different than watching cockfights and a group of drunk men screaming at roosters trying to kill one another, as you do at the *gallera* (cockfight ring)," he said.

Dating from as early as Roman times, cockfighting was also a popular sport in the United States, particularly during Colonial times. To prepare for the game, *galleros* or "cockers" (men involved in the game) invested much in the care of their fighting roosters. They fed them a special diet, housed them in special barns, and trained them in preparation for matches. They also strapped metal spurs with pointed blades to their gamecocks' legs as weapons to help them prevail in the match.

On his correspondence home, Antonio addressed his occasional travels to New York City, but only in general. He did not want to give his family the impression that he was endeavoring into frivolous affairs, when in fact he should be studying and perfecting his English.

As they read Antonio's letter, Manuel and Etervina noticed their son sounded like a changed man, already. This comforted them in their decision of sending Antonio to New York.

. . .

Antonio was fascinated by the foliage change from summer to fall, as he had not seen this metamorphosis back home in the tropics. He had, however, witnessed the *flamboyanes* (jacarandas) bloom between the months of May and August and the *trinitaria* (bouganvilea) flower from summer to fall. Other flowering trees in Puerto Rico, such as the *roble* (oak) and the *maga* (related to the hibiscus) produced flowers all year long. It was "eternal spring" in the island, and this was beautiful, but Antonio had never seen the leaves change color as they did in Schoharie.

The sugar maple trees were a spectacular orange, and the dogwoods and sumacs displayed bright reddish and purplish hues. These colors made a striking contrast with the evergreen pine trees. Antonio was pleased to be able to still see green in the foliage. It anchored him back to the perennial green landscape of the valleys of Comerío in his homeland.

"The snowfall is magical," he wrote to his parents.

His eyes had not seen anything like it, other than the tobacco fields covered with the white canvas that dressed the mountains along the *La Plata River* in the snow color. Antonio was so cold! He had to learn to dress properly, so he would not "freeze to death," as he wrote to his parents on more than one occasion.

While Antonio wrote home about everything new to him, he did not say much about Bessie, Mrs. Kromer's daughter, who had become his favorite English tutor. He did not highlight her in his correspondence, perhaps because he was already falling for Bessie, and this would be quite the scandal back home.

No, he would not cause unnecessary worry. They did not need to know, at least for now. He only referred to "his tutor" in the most generic terms. But somehow Etervina would find out. He mentioned his tutor much too often on his letters. A mother knows.

With grace, Etervina sent a glass vase as a gift to Mrs. Kromer and Bessie from the Pontón family in appreciation for "taking such good care" of Antonio, who was "all alone in a new country, facing a different language and a different culture."

Chapter 19. Bessie

Bessie S. Kromer was a young grade school teacher who had lived in Schoharie most of her life. In fact, she had never left the state of New York.

Bessie was neither too tall nor too short. She had light brown wavy hair and big round brown eyes; her skin was fair, and she had the kindest smile. She often wore conservative long, buttoned-up dresses in a solid color. Sometimes she wore bonnets, like her mother, but she also wore her hair in a low Victorian bun, which she adorned with a wrap-around braid. And she loved elegant hats.

When Antonio arrived to Schoharie in July of 1911, Bessie was 22 years old and would turn 23 that coming November 10th. As she was studying while working, she would return home to 27 Main Street on weekends to spend time with her mother Nora and brother Charles, Jr., two years younger than her. Her father, Charles C. Kromer, former Captain of the Company G, 3rd New York Calvary during the Civil War, had just passed away that year.

Although Mrs. Kromer was still collecting the war pension from her husband's service, and she made earnings as a milliner making hats from home, times were tough for Bessie's family, still mourning the loss of Captain Kromer. Bessie's younger brother Charles worked as a salesman in a grocery store and also helped support the household. He left high school after his father passed, just two years shy of completing it.

Bessie helped to support her family with her teacher salary and the extra few dollars she made as an English tutor. She was beautiful, intelligent and independent. She was also outspoken, like her mother, except when she was in her mother's presence. Mrs. Kromer had a strong influence on her daughter. And although Bessie often got away with disregarding her mother's wishes, sometimes Bessie had no choice but to comply with her commands.

The Kromer women were strong-minded.

Bessie's strength permeated in part from her Dutch ancestry. She descended from the original founders of Schoharie, who settled there in the early 18th century as farmers. Her ancestor Teunis Eckerson was a private in the 15th Regiment, Albany County, New York Militia, during the American Revolution. Her family was highly patriotic and followed the Lutheran faith.

Things would have been so different had Bessie and Antonio not crossed paths!

Chapter 20. The Spell

Bessie tutored Antonio in English when she came home on weekends. He would study during the week and sometimes visit other tutors in town. Mrs. Gebhardt, a neighbor, and Reverend Karg, Pastor of the Schoharie Lutheran Church, also helped Antonio with his lessons and conversational English practice.

Most of the time, if the weather allowed, Bessie would teach Antonio in the back porch of the house. Antonio was the only boarder, and Bessie's brother Charles was often away at work at the grocery store.

Bessie's mother Nora was an active woman. Besides making hats, she tended to her elderly mother, who still lived by herself down the street, attended church activities during the week, did the groceries, and participated in meetings of the Daughters of the American Revolution. "DAR," as they called the group, was a women's service organization founded in 1890 in Washington D.C. "dedicated to promoting patriotism, preserving American history, and securing America's future through better education for children." The Schoharie DAR Chapter was fairly new, organized in 1910. Mrs. Kromer was quite fond of the group, not only due to Captain Kromer's service, but also because of her pride in their ancestors' role in the revolution. She also enjoyed socializing with the village ladies, who spent a good time talking about anything and everything.

. . .

To study, Bessie and Antonio sat on a round white iron coffee table with a wooden top decorated with a yellow and blue mosaic that was more suitable for having tea than anything else.

It was quiet and peaceful there.

"Good day, Mr. Pontón. How is the assignment coming along?"

90

Bessie asked her pupil.

"Bery wel, Bery wel, Mees Besi," Antonio responded. "I finis. Tek luhk if ju wan! But ju chood cal me Antonio, not Meester Pontón! I am not my grandfather, ju kno!"

She paused.

"It looks good, Mr. Pontón. You have done a great job!" she said, after reviewing the work and ignoring his first-name plea.

He noticed she kept her distance.

"Today, I will read to you," she continued, "so we can practice pronunciation. You are doing *very well*, not *bery wel. ¿Entiende?*"

"Jehs," he said. "Bery wel. No … *very* wel. Rite?"

"Yes, close enough," she said. "But it is not *jehs*. The *y* sounds like *yah*. Get it? I know it is a new sound you do not have in Spanish. But you will learn. Listen to me carefully now."

When Bessie read to him, Antonio's piercing light green eyes fixed on her, and he would often lose focus away from his lesson. He admired her ability to teach, and he loved the sound of her voice and her eloquence. She was patient, kind, educated, and dedicated to making sure he understood each lesson.

Bessie was also drawn to her pupil. He was handsome and educated. She pictured him as a lawyer, "a good catch" for marriage, even though he was "a Spaniard," "a Porto Rican."

Antonio knew she was attracted to him. Their chemistry was evident.

On one occasion, Antonio interrupted Bessie's teachings with a sense of urgency: "Wait! Somesin wron!" he said with his strong Spanish accent.

Startled by Antonio's behavior, Bessie looked at him with her big brown eyes wide open, almost feeling her heart stop for a moment, wondering what she did to upset him.

"I hav to kol hehben becos angel escape!" he said, alarmed.

Her heart now pounding on her chest, Bessie looked at her surroundings for a split second, as though searching for the missing angel.

Antonio began laughing out loud.

Bessie came to her senses within seconds, realizing that he meant to compliment her with a Spanish *piropo* or pick-up line. She blushed like the reddest rose.

Bessie enjoyed the good humor, but she needed to ensure he

respected her. She raised her eyebrows and looked straight into Antonio's green eyes, as though she was about to scold one of her young students.

"Mr. Pontón, you have to stop this nonsense and focus on your lesson! Otherwise, you will never be ready for law school!" she said.

Antonio smiled back at her and placed his right hand over hers, to calm her down. She was even prettier when she was serious.

"Mees Besi, *¡No lo puedo evitar!* I can't help it! *¡Es usted preciosa!* Ju are so beeutifool!" He took his pencil and wrote down on his notebook, "Bessie," and drew a big heart around her name. Then, he added his name right below hers, and in between both names, he wrote the letter *y* (and). Inside the heart he had just drawn, it now read: *"Bessie y Antonio."*

Bessie sighed.

Her face blushing and her heart pounding, she replied, "I think we are done for the day, Mr. Pontón. There is no use!"

In silence, she retrieved her books and lesson papers from the table, returned them to her bag, rushed back into the house, and went upstairs, straight to her room.

Antonio sat on his chair, looking down, shaking his head left and right, his heart beating fast. He knew he had crossed the line. But he had to tell her. Bessie walking out on Antonio made him feel that he wanted her so much more.

The chase had begun.

. . .

Sunday morning, after rising early to prepare for church, Bessie was drawn to the back porch. Her mother Nora and her brother Charles had left earlier for choir practice. On top of the small round table where she and Antonio were studying the day before, there was a red rose and an ivory envelope addressed to Bessie. Her brown eyes scanned around to make sure no one was watching, and she rushed to open the envelope. Inside, there was a small piece of thin paper, folded in half, with some writing on it.

Her curiosity overcame her. She unfolded the note in haste.

It read, "Miss Bessie. Please forgive me if I have offended you. *¡Perdóneme, por favor! Su admirador, Antonio."* (Please forgive me! Your admirer, Antonio.")

Bessie's heart began beating faster; she rushed to return the note into its envelope, and she placed it in her skirt's pocket. She lifted the red rose by the stem with her right hand, careful to avoid the thorns, and with her left hand she cradled the delicate bud that had just began to open, bringing it close to her nose. It was still moist, and its scent was as no other rose she had ever sensed before.

Her heart now pounding, a strange feeling of combined fear and happiness invaded her. She took a deep breath. Her lungs filled with fresh air. An invigorating rush of electricity all over her body overcame her.

"So, is this how falling in love feels?" she thought.

She knew the answer.

. . .

Over time, Bessie grew fonder of Antonio every time she saw him; his wavy ash-blond hair, his green eyes, his *piropos* ... and his accent. He was bold and vulnerable at the same time, passionate, intelligent, and he went out of his way to make sure that she knew how much he liked her. How much she meant to him. He fought to conquer her heart.

And she loved the attention.

This was a relationship that had "trouble" written all over, she thought. She could not fall in love with him. To start, Antonio was "a Spaniard." He was Catholic, and she was Lutheran. She did not know anything about him, his family, or his past, but for his documents and his mother's kind letter and gift. In the short time he had been in town, rumors were that he was of noble descent, and that his family back in Puerto Rico was wealthy. She also heard he had "a weakness for the ladies."

"What if he had a serious relationship back home?" she thought.

She could not put herself in a position to become just one more of his lovers. Her self-respect had to take precedence. She would not fall victim to a *Giacomo Girolamo Casanova*, the 18th Century Venetian womanizer she had read about. No. Their relationship would not work. She should marry a man who resembled her father.

"Would father approve of Antonio if he were alive?" she thought.

She knew, in all probability, he would not. And her mother would not, either. Antonio's culture was not like her family's. He would not fit in. He was not like them.

That night, she went to bed with troubled thoughts about Antonio.

. . .

Antonio and Bessie enjoyed a picnic at *Lasell Park*. It was a spring sunny day. They rested on a plaid blue, yellow and white blanket, leaning against each other, shoulder-to-shoulder, laughing and holding hands amorously. The soft breeze, the sounds of nature and the aroma of the flowers soothed them.

They looked into each other's eyes and there was complete silence.

Antonio's face came closer to hers, and he placed a gentle kiss on her moist lips. He whispered her name, "Besi," as only he could pronounce it.

He cast the spell.

She closed her eyes. Her heartbeat gained speed. Never had she felt this way in her entire existence.

Antonio's left hand moved from her cheek down to her neck, the tips of his fingers caressing her soft skin. Down to her shoulder, navigating inch-by-inch, slowly, down to her waist.

They kissed in a passionate embrace. Again and again they breathed each other's air and tasted the sweet nectar of each other's lips. The adrenaline rushed through her veins.

He is the one! She never wanted this moment to end.

He continued kissing her on her neck.

"Oh, Besi," he whispered as he moved his lips towards her chest. "I so want to make love to you!"

His hand sailed from her hip to her left breast, and he began caressing it as he kissed her lips.

"I want you, too, Antonio," she said.

He began to unbutton her shirt, as he tasted her lips. And she let him. She wanted more.

"Oh, Antonio!" she said. "I love you!"

"I love you, too," he said.

"Bessie! Bessie!"

. . .

Bessie awakened to her mother's screechy voice, calling her name out loud. "Bessie! Bessie! Wake up! What has gotten into you?" Mrs. Kromer said.

"This has not happened to you since you were a little girl!"

Bessie had overslept.

Chapter 21. Mr. and Mrs. Fernández

Against the force behind her better instincts, Bessie and Antonio began courting not long after she started tutoring him. His English much improved, as he had a strong incentive.

During lessons she scribbled on his notebook "*Yo te amo*. I love you."

And he felt real love for the first time ever. It was different this time. She was his true love. He had found her. He had found her, at last.

The lovers were avid sightseers, and they often visited the Schoharie historical landmarks such as the *Old Stone Fort*, the *Iron Bridge*, *Howe Caverns*, and *Lasell Park*. They also admired the sights of *Terrace Mountain*.

Bessie could not help herself. She had to teach Antonio about her town's rich history.

"Do you know who Samuel Langhorne Clemens is, Antonio?" Bessie asked.

"No, chood I?" he said.

"He is best known as Mark Twain, the author of *The Adventures of Tom Sawyer*," she said.

"I have herd of the story, but I hav not red the booc," he said.

"Well, you should read it," she said. "It is excellent reading. An American classic. Mark Twain worked in Schoharie for a while," she said.

"Is that so?" he said.

"Yes, he worked as a brakeman on the Schoharie railroad station on Depot Street the winter of 1879, three years after he wrote his famous book," Bessie said.

"Why would he do that, a famos author?" Antonio asked.

"A self-published author, I should add," she said. "He had his own publishing company, too. Well, he hired his nephew by marriage to

96

run it."

"Really?" he said.

"Yes. He worked as a miner for a long time, and in the meanwhile, he wrote," she said. "He made a small fortune with his publications, but he was not good with money, so he went bankrupt."

"He did?" said Antonio.

"But he recovered, and he ended up paying his creditors even though he was not legally required to do so. What do you think about that?" she asked.

"I think he was an honorable man," Antonio responded. "It's the right thing to do. This is what my father believes, also. A man chood not die leaving debts."

"Mark Twain was born when Halley's Comet arrived, and he predicted with humor that he would die when the comet returned, that he would *go out with it*," Bessie continued her 'lesson.' "And he did as promised. He passed away a day after the comet's return, just last year in 1910," she said.

Bessie was full of stories to tell. They were all fascinating to him.

And he would go to the end of the world for her.

The couple traveled to New York City often. Antonio once told friends that Bessie and he would travel "as husband and wife" and stayed in hotels overnight under the name of "Mr. and Mrs. Fernández." Fernández was his father Manuel's maternal last name.

. . .

On her bedroom dresser, Bessie had a photograph of Antonio and her together, taken during one of their visits to Coney Island. They posed on what appeared to be the back of a railroad car. She wore an elegant black dress and a beautiful hat with flowers on it. He was handsome, dressed up in a dark suit and tie.

He had the same photo on his bedroom dresser.

Coney Island was an established vacation destination with resorts, rides and bathhouses, located on the southwestern part of Brooklyn, in New York City. Antonio and Bessie visited Coney Island after "the Dreamland fire" of May 1911. The site was accessible by railroad streetcar, and before the piers were consumed by the fire, by steamboat. Dreamland was not rebuilt after the fire, but post-fire visitors could still visit Steeplechase Park, where they rode wooden horses around the park on a steel track, went up and down on the Ferris wheel, and enjoyed scale models of world landmarks, such as the Eiffel Tower and The Palace of Westminster's clock tower, containing the Big Ben.

Vacationers could also visit *Luna Park, The Bowery, The Nickel Empire* freak show (built over the Dreamland grounds after the fire) and the *Cake Walk*, among many other attractions. Some travelers targeted the beach, if they could afford the expensive private access and dressed properly to avoid fines or even arrest for "indecent exposure," levied on those who wore "revealing bathing suits."

While at Luna Park, Bessie told Antonio about the unfortunate fate of Topsy, an elephant the circus businessman Adam Forepaugh brought to the United States as a baby. The elephant was later employed when it was older during the construction of the park. Around 1903, Topsy was put down at Luna Park because it had become aggressive. Bessie was just a child back then, and she recalled being upset and disgusted at how the poor elephant was treated.

"Topsy the elephant killed three men over the course of three years," she told Antonio. "But I often wonder about what made it snap," she said.

"Was it crasy?" he asked.

"I don't know. But I think it just had enough. I read one handler Topsy killed had just fed the elephant a lit cigarette. The two other handlers repeatedly poked it with pitchforks," she said.

"That's tu bad," he said.

"What was the dear going to do, continue to take the abuse?" Bessie said, upset. "There is no way I would endure the abuse," she added. "If I were Topsy, with certainty, I would have reacted as the elephant did! Topsy was just defending itself!" she said.

"How was the elephant 'put down,' as you say?" asked Antonio.

"At first, there were talks about hanging the poor elephant," she said, "but the Society for the Prevention of Cruelty to Animals opposed," Bessie continued. "Then, Mr. Thomas Edison, the inventor and owner of Edison Works, the electrical company in Schenectady, proposed executing Topsy with electricity, just like they do with humans sentenced to death for murder," she said, distraught at Edison's idea.

"What happened then?" he asked, thirsty for the gruesome details.

"Do you really want to know more about how the poor living and breathing creature was killed?" Bessie asked Antonio, somewhat surprised at his curiosity.

"Jhes! I mean ... Yes!" he begged with excitement, while trying to get a hold of his pronunciation.

"Well, Antonio," she said. "They first poisoned it with cyanide-laced carrots, and then they fried it with electricity!" she revealed.

Antonio paused.

For a moment, he put himself in place of the animal and imagined how it must have felt while it was "fried by electricity," as Bessie put it. He released the awful thought within a second.

"*Fried?*" he asked. "How do ju fry an elephant with electricity?"

"They tied electrodes to its body and used the park's power generator to electrocute it," she said.

He was silent.

"And if the cyanide and the electricity were not enough," Bessie sighed, "they strangled it for ten minutes using donkeys pulling on a hawser about its neck. You know, to make sure that it was flat dead!" she said, with sarcasm.

By now, it was clear that the event had scarred Bessie.

Antonio listened.

"Edison filmed the whole thing!" Bessie continued. "So if it would amuse you to locate the film somewhere and see it for yourself, I suppose you could!" she challenged him.

"Why did they kill the elephant using electricity?" Antonio asked. "Wasn't there another way?"

She responded, "They said it would not hurt the animal. I believe Mr. Edison's employees had gone all over the country electrocuting dogs and cats, horses and cows too, to show how Mr. Westinghouse's dangerous 'alternating current' was so much more harmful than Mr. Edison's 'direct current.' It was all about the competition between the two men and their businesses. It was, as it has always has been, all about money and power."

"But," Antonio said, looking at the situation from a scientific perspective. "Besi, from a seyens point of view, I find the story fascinatin."

"Fascinating?" she asked, in awe.

"I mean," he continued. "I consider becoming a doctor before I decide on becoming a lawjer. And I kno animals are often sacrificed to benefit seyens."

Bessie believed that animals had rights, just as people did. To her, there was no justification for killing in the name of science.

"I don't find the scientific aspect of killing fascinating at all. Humans can be monsters," Bessie said to Antonio. "It is such a waste of a life to kill a living being that has no way of telling right from wrong, a defenseless creature with limited capacity and a troubled past," Bessie added.

Bessie paused for a moment and then continued defending Topsy, as a defense attorney would his criminal client.

"They themselves turned Topsy into what it had become, taking it from its mother as such an early age, only to abuse it. It was traumatized. Perhaps it was even ill in its head. They definitively cornered it! Yet, they killed the poor elephant when it acted just as expected. It does not make any sense! They should have just moved it to a zoo or a sanctuary, where it could not harm anyone, and no one could harm it," she said, volunteering a just punishment for Topsy.

With compassion, but still aggravated, Bessie raised her eyes to the skies, as though speaking to Topsy in the heavens, and said, "It must have suffered so! I don't care that they said that it died 'without a trumpet or a groan.' I heard that when they flipped the switch and the thousands of volts of electricity ran through its veins, the poor animal cried in pain, opening its big green eyes, its body shaken by the current, and then it just plummeted to the ground, all six tons of it!"

Although fascinated by the tale, Antonio was sensitive to Bessie's feelings. He remained silent.

Bessie then turned to Antonio with frustration, as though expecting him to say something in return, in sympathy for Topsy.

But his lips were sealed. He knew better than to utter one more word.

She then said, "How would you like that done to you! People are just sadists! Can you believe that over a thousand people came to watch the execution?" She chastised the action of turning the electrocution into a spectacle and charging an entrance fee.

"Pure Nonsense!" she added to her soliloquy.

Antonio tried to dissipate Bessie's anger by suggesting they get their photograph taken. She agreed, and so they walked to one of the park's photo booths, which resembled the back of a railroad wagon. They both had some trouble smiling for the camera, given the serious exchange they just had.

After taking their photograph, Antonio purchased six copies, three for each of them. He planned to send one to his parents. They continued strolling through the park.

Bessie looked down, in silence, still thinking about Topsy.

Just when Antonio thought Bessie was letting go of the story for good, she raised it to another level.

"Same goes for the execution of humans," she said, bringing up the topic of death penalty and the execution of human beings.

"We ourselves become murderers when we execute people. Who are we to kill them, when they themselves are being punished for killing? Society is totally hypocritical. We use a crime to punish the same crime we condemn!" She went on mocking the measure. "Killing is killing, period. There is no justification. We should know better. Killing is a sin!"

As a prospective law student, the arguments of retribution, deterrence and societal benefit as justifications for executing humans, or self-defense or insanity as criminal excuses for an accused criminal, flashed through Antonio's mind. But he knew better than to debate the heated topic of death penalty with Bessie and perpetuate her agony. Not a chance. She was already visibly affected by the taking of a life, even if it was that of an animal. It was obvious that she was still impacted by Topsy's fate, perhaps because she had experienced the sad news when she was a child.

Antonio limited himself to nod in her support.

"Poor Topsy," he said, trying to empathize and seal away the awkwardness.

He reached out to Bessie. Playful, he placed his left arm over her shoulders and brought her body towards his.

He then stopped walking and looked at her. With the side of his curled right index finger under her chin, he lifted her face to meet her gaze and kissed her forehead.

"Let's go to the moon!" Antonio suggested, smiling and changing the dreadful subject for good.

Looking into Antonio's green eyes, Bessie abandoned her troubled expression and a smile began to appear on her face. She agreed with him.

"I am sorry," she said. "We are at Coney Island, a place to have fun and be happy, not sad!"

Antonio smiled and said, "That's right!"

With her arm chained to his, the couple paced towards the famous "A Trip to the Moon" ride and lined up to board the spacecraft "Luna."

Chapter 22. To Albany

Antonio's application to Albany Law School had been accepted to start as soon as the fall of 1911, but since he needed to become more fluent in the English language he decided to begin law school on September of 1912, instead. He was scheduled to graduate with the Class of 1915.

The summer after the tragic sinking of the *RMS Titanic* on April 15, 1912, Antonio began plans to secure an apartment in Albany and move out of the Kromer boarding house in Schoharie. He rented an apartment from Mrs. Chamberlain in her building at 52 Clinton Avenue, a small three-story building with a basement and an attic, part of a block of red brick buildings with similar structure built in 1891. His apartment had a small gas kitchen and a private room, but the bathroom was shared among the boarders.

Antonio had to walk about two miles to Albany Law School from his new apartment. His walking route to school took him about half an hour at a fast pace, but sometimes he slowed down while going through Washington Park.

He looked forward to strolling down the park. It was lovely and peaceful. Sometimes, if the weather was not too cold and it was sunny, he studied there.

"Washington Park's wooden lake house is as a pearl on the corner of the oyster-shaped lake," he wrote once to his parents. It sounded a bit like poetry. Etervina read between the lines. She knew her son had to be in love to write with such inspiration.

"The *King Memorial Fountain* of Moses is so impressive and powerful, and the newer *Soldier's and Sailor's* monument pays tribute to the bravery of military men. Washington Park's design is perfect," he wrote. "It is one of my favorite places here."

During his walks to school, the elm trees came to life and accompanied Antonio all the way up to when he crossed Madison

Avenue and took New Scotland Avenue to arrive at Albany Law School.

He would close his eyes and feel the breeze, pretending it was sent by the trees to caress his face as he walked through the park.

"Ahh," he thought. "So peaceful."

The trees' embrace gave him strength before the start of a busy day of class. He never had trouble being in harmony with nature.

Chapter 23. Albany Law School

Albany Law School was established in 1851 and was among the oldest institutions of its kind in the United States. By 1912, many outstanding attorneys had graduated from Albany Law School and represented the school well in the executive, judicial and legislative departments of New York and other states, as well as the federal government. The school became a part of Union University in 1873, and it was on its 62nd year as a law school when Antonio was accepted.

"September 12, 1912, Albany Law School. Dear Family," Antonio wrote. "The law school facilities afforded to the students here are unsurpassed. We have access to large classrooms, a lounge, an athletic facility, and the school's library, which is open all hours. The students could also use the state law library, the largest in the United States, featuring over 65,000 volumes. The law school also has fraternities, in addition to basketball and baseball teams, and a publication called *The Albany Law School Journal*."

Manuel and Etervina felt assured their money was well invested. Albany Law School was indeed one of the best.

Antonio was one of 47 students admitted in 1911. He, among many others, was intimidated by the formality of being in a law school of such standing. Being there brought out every weakness he could experience about himself, as he tried to build a new "safety net" in this new environment, which promised to be challenging. He noticed his lack of confidence was a common denominator across first-year students, and this placed him at ease, if only for moments at a time. Despite his anxiety, Antonio was excited to be at Albany Law School. He was the only one in his family to endeavor into a professional career. This levied pressure on him to do well, but he wished to make Manuel and Etervina proud.

There was already a set precedent of Puerto Rican students

attending Albany Law School. This trend began not long after the Spanish-American War. The first to attend was Pedro G. Amador of Camuy, Class of 1902. Joining the next class were José Ramos Casellas from Manatí and Pedro E. Ramírez of Mayagüez. Class prophet Leopoldo Feliú of San Germán graduated in 1906, having distinguished himself by writing the best final thesis. José López Acosta, also from Manatí, married Clarissa B. Pritchard, another law student. José Sabater, Class of 1909, became a judge of the Superior Court in Puerto Rico. More than two-dozen Puerto Ricans attended the school over a twenty-year period during Dean J. Newton Fiero's administration.

Dean J. Newton Fiero (b 1847), a man of Dutch and Spanish ancestry and a graduate of Union College himself, had held the deanship since 1895 and would stay as Dean until 1924. He spoke to Antonio's class during the Freshmen Welcoming Ceremony. Dean Fiero extended the law school program of studies from one to two to three years and introduced a legal ethics component. He authored a number of law books, and his knowledge of state law and procedure was unsurpassed. Newton Fiero was also one of the professors at the school, teaching *The Law of Procedure, Equity, Torts,* and *Evidence.*

Antonio could not stop thinking about Dean Fiero's words during his welcoming speech, "Look to your left; now to your right. One of you will not be here in 1915!" These words were used to intimidate freshman law students to draw their attention to the importance of being diligent in their forthcoming studies. They still are.

The workload would prove to be unbearable for many.

The curriculum was comprehensive. Lewis R. Parker taught *The Law of Bailments, Bills and Notes, Guaranty and Suretyship,* and *Constitutional Law.* Fletcher W. Battershall taught *Elementary Law* and *Domestic Relations.* Frank White taught *The Law of Corporations.* George Lawyer taught *The Law of Contracts, Personal Property and Sales,* and *Bankruptcy.* Frank B. Gilbert taught *Real Property, Legislation,* and *Statutory Construction.* Jacob C. E. Scott taught *Criminal Law.* Frederick W. Cameron taught *Patents, Copyright, and "Trade-Marks."* Charles J. Herrick taught *Civil Law, International Law,* and *Conflict of Laws.* The following judges lectured: Hon. Alton B. Parker on *Development of the Law,* Hon. Irvin G. Vann on *Insurance,* Hon. William Werner on *Constitutional Law,* and Hon. Alden Chester on *The Federal Judicial System.* Frederick D.

Colson lectured on *Books and their Uses*.

To graduate with a degree in law, Antonio and all other Albany Law School students had to comply with five strict requirements: (1) Complete four years (or their equivalent) of work of a grade above the elementary or grammar school before beginning the course of study; (2) Complete three full years of law school; (3) Complete the course in residency in no less than one year; (4) Be of good moral character; and (5) Be at least 21 years of age.

The annual tuition cost was $110, matriculation was $10, and the graduation fee was $10. Books could be pricey, but the library was an alternative to purchasing. There were also "Hornbooks" the students could purchase to help summarize the class topics and facilitate studying. The *West Publishing Company* offered about 32 of them for sale at $3.79 each.

"Mr. John Charles Watson, the school's Registrar here at Albany Law School, is an obliging individual," Antonio wrote. "He recently graduated from Albany Law School himself, having replaced the former Registrar, John J. Hughes, who passed away in 1911. Mr. Watson is a trustworthy man. He is supportive to students in their studies."

Indeed, Watson helped when Antonio had trouble coping with some of his schoolwork, and when he was absent from class due to his frequent headaches.

Antonio welcomed the opportunity to release some school anxiety and go out with his classmates every now and again. "It is customary for the students, following an exam, to gather at *Garrity's* for a drink," he wrote to Manuel and Etervina. "From time to time, the professor would join us, often after an exam."

On occasion, Antonio mentioned in his letters various law students he had befriended. "Stanley Bliss, one year my senior, is a bright student who often assists me with advice." Bliss clerked for attorney DeWitt the summer of 1911 and shared his experience with Antonio. He invited Antonio to his commencement ceremonies on June 5, 1912.

After he attended commencement in 1912, Antonio was fueled with excitement and looked forward to his own graduation in 1915 and to honor his father's last name among the graduates.

"Some students who completed law school in 1912 were allowed to attend the commencement ceremonies with their graduating class, but they were not given their degree because they were not twenty-one years old yet," Antonio wrote. "Instead, they were awarded a 'graduation certificate' or 'certificate of attendance.' They would receive their degree when they turn twenty-one. Among them is a student by the name of Robert H. Jackson, who other students say has a brilliant mind."

Indeed, after graduating from Albany Law School, Robert H. Jackson (b 1892) became a leading American lawyer, judge and writer. He served as a United States Supreme Court Justice from 1941 until 1954. During 1945-46, Justice Jackson designed the international trial process and became the chief prosecutor of the surviving Nazi leaders at Nuremberg, Germany.

"Among the students under twenty-one are the twin sisters by the name of Clara and Clarissa Pritchard. Clarissa is the one who married one of the Puerto Rican students, López from the town Manatí," he wrote. "They look quite young," Antonio commented. "Although there are few women in the class, there are some women graduating from law school here," he remarked, surprised to some extent at the presence of women in the law classroom.

There were also some Puerto Rican students who attended commencement with Bliss, Jackson and the twin sisters. They volunteered some guidance from time to time and interacted with Antonio on a social basis: Ulpiano Crespo, Jr. from Añasco, the brothers José and Mateo Fajardo from Mayagüez, and Plinio Castro from Cabo Rojo. Eugene Vera, also from Puerto Rico, sometimes studied with Antonio. Antonio López was a student from San Juan. Among his American friends was C.H. Hersey, who roomed in the same building as Antonio did.

. . .

Witnessing the leaves change in color during autumn was a special privilege for Antonio. One day, he took a few leaves and stuffed them in an envelope so his parents could see the colors.

"Some of the leaves have the yellow-reddish color of tobacco leaves when they are ready for harvesting," he wrote. "Don't you think?"

It felt gloomy when the trees lost their leaves and turned bare, he thought, although this signaled that the snow was near. "I love the snow, at least at the beginning, when it is powder white." It was mesmerizing to watch the snowfall. The coldest precipitation he had experienced back home was hail, and this ruined the crops.

"Striding through the dirty slush on the street after the snow is a few days old is most unpleasant, though," he wrote. When the slush stained his lace-up shoes, Antonio learned the hard way that it was best to purchase flaps to protect his shoes from the weather, or wear leather boots. He read about a company in Maine called *L.L. Bean*. It crafted special boots for hunters and had just made them available for sale. It seemed these new boots would be practical for walking to school in the slush, but their appearance was too casual, in Antonio's opinion.

"The L.L. Bean boots are a great idea, but they would not be fitting attire for law school," he wrote home. "All law school students must wear proper dress for class."

In the classroom, Antonio wore *Livingston* black trousers, a tombstone shirt, a *Stafford* vest, a tie or a bow, *Y-Back* braces, a *Callahan* frock coat, and of course, a felt *derby*. Also, he always carried the gold pocket watch and chain his mother Etervina got for him all the way from Spain as a "good luck" charm before he left Puerto Rico.

Antonio Pontón was an elegant law student.

. . .

The Class of 1912 was the last class to graduate after only two years of law school. Subsequent classes would have to undergo three years of classes before graduation, a new change implemented by the school to expand its legal theory curriculum. Antonio told his parents that if he only had begun school one year earlier, the year he was actually admitted, he would have spared them one year of tuition expenses. But he did not know this change was coming.

Truth be told, more than tuition savings, Antonio's fate would have taken a much different turn if he had begun law school in 1911.

He would not have crossed paths with Bessie S. Kromer and her mother.

Chapter 24. The Medieval Dungeon

Antonio and Bessie continued their courtship after he began law school. They wrote to each other often and telephoned as much as possible. They traveled together on some weekends and holidays, if time allowed, and sometimes he would skip studying just so he could see her. The romance became quite a distraction for Antonio, who was already finding it difficult to concentrate on his studies, due to the inherent workload and his deteriorating health.

Antonio's headaches were escalating, at times consuming him, and he was no longer able to process and retain all the information he was required to learn for class. He much preferred to be with Bessie than in "the medieval dungeon," as he called the classroom.

Her voice was the calming force to his tempestuous mind.

Professors at Albany Law School taught the law using *The Case Method* combined with *The Socratic Method*. When questioned in class by a professor using the Socratic Method Antonio opened up his green eyes wide and paralyzed in fear. Everything and anything he studied the day before would vanish from his memory in an instant. Nerves took over. His English would scramble in his mind.

When called, he often said, "I pass," the term to let the professor know he was not prepared. He felt compelled to do this, even if he was prepared. He was too embarrassed to follow suit after being called. After noting Antonio's name on his student participation chart, the professor would move on to another "victim."

"Dear Family," Antonio wrote. "At Albany Law School, professors call on a student at random and ask about a particular issue or argument in an assigned case. The student 'called on' has to summarize the case and issue at hand to demonstrate his understanding of the case and applicable law. If the student has indeed read the case and could articulate the issue and the rule of law, the professor would continue by asking the student's opinion about the argument and the conclusion of the case. The professor then plays 'devil's advocate' inviting opposing views by other students. The professor proceeds to compel the first student to present arguments to rebut those opposing views. The same 'back and forth' exercise takes place for every class. The same story repeats daily 'like Chinese torture.' The professor notes who is prepared and who is not, and the student's participation in this exercise, along with the tests grades, contributes to the student's final grade in the course. This exercise is nerve-wrecking!"

Manuel and Etervina felt their son's anxiety through the ink in his letters.

"I am required to read hundreds of pages of cases every day, and the professors expect all students to not only read the material but to also memorize the facts, the law, and the arguments of the case for the next day's class discussion. They recommend reading the material three times to ensure full preparation. All the work has to be accomplished in one afternoon after class ends for the day, in preparation for the next day. Most students do not find time to read the material once, let alone three times," his letter continued. "In addition to the daily requirement, we test every week for each class and also at the end of the term."

Antonio could not keep up and was overwhelmed with the amount of material. He could not remember the applicable case law well enough to answer the many questions from his professors.

"The class exercise makes me feel as though I am being tortured in a 'medieval dungeon.' The recurrent class affair is like being cross-examined in a courtroom. The practice is demeaning to the students, and I do not find any enjoyment in this exercise, at all. I much prefer to study and be tested, not be grilled," he wrote. "But I guess this is a new approach. Some of my classmates share my sentiments, while others find that the Socratic and Case methods are intellectually stimulating, and they are learning how to think on their feet, as a lawyer should think in a courtroom."

Manuel and Etervina were worried. They knew Antonio did not do well under severe pressure. They wrote to their son words of encouragement, saying that all students were probably in his position, anxious and tired, but to stay put. He would get used to the discipline. The bar was set high, but it was attainable. Other Puerto Rican students had successfully gone through the program. The students were expected to strive their best, and they would be better lawyers for it.

The language barrier, the insurmountable amount of classwork, his health problems, and his constant thinking about Bessie raised a mountain too high for Antonio to climb.

The pressure buildup was agonizing.

Part III. The Crime

"Pardon me for this resolution ... I know that this will be a disgrace that I bring to my people, but I cannot help it. Love is the blame for it. I go in peace ... pray for me ... good-bye all."

- Antonio Pontón,
in a suicide letter addressed to the Albany Law School Registrar,
September 1914

Chapter 25. Crumbling Down

Although he passed all his first-year courses in law school, known to be the most challenging, Antonio had to retake some of his second-year courses.

He was now behind.

To make matters worse, Bessie was taking him to the heavens one day, but the next day she would drop him all the way down into hell, telling him that she needed some time alone and did not want to see him for some time. Not long after that episode, she would call or write to him again, telling him she missed him and wanted to get back together forever. And then again, she would make excuses to not see him.

"Besi, I am going to transfer to Harvard University. I cannot bear the pressuar of school and our relationchip," said Antonio. "It's like the *Rough Riders* ride. I can't take it."

The *Rough Riders* was one of the roller coaster rides in Coney Island, which showcased a Spanish-American War theme upon coaster ascent. The ride had malfunctioned during the 60-feet drop, killing some of the passengers.

"With your poor grades you will not get the transfer, Antonio. I beg you. Stay. I promise, we will always be together," she assured him. "Forever."

"I am confused, Besi. Ju break up with me, then call me back. Then break up again. I can't bear it. I can't," Antonio said. "You are killing me, I tell ju!"

"I am struggling with mother's pressures to end our relationchip. But I love you! I will stay with you despite her. Forever. I promise you!" she repeated. "I will find a way!"

Antonio wanted to believe Bessie, and he agreed to continue together, only for the vicious cycle to repeat.

The unstable relationship with Bessie and the pressures of law

114

school continued to consume Antonio. He feared that he was going to lose her. It was a matter of time. And he did not see a way to recover in school. How was he going to tell his father Manuel he was failing? He was getting sicker, and his world was crumbling down.

Antonio became severely depressed.

. . .

One morning, Mrs. Chamberlain, Antonio's landlady, a gray-haired English lady in her sixties with a big mole on her right cheek, smelled the odor of gas coming from Antonio's apartment. She knocked at the door calling his name in her very deep but 'ringy' voice.

"Mr. Pontón!" she called. He did not answer. She knocked for about two more minutes, until he opened the door.

"Jehs, Meeses Chimberlen," a hesitant Antonio responded.

The door ajar, the pungent odor of propane gas coming from the apartment swirled inside the English landlady's nostrils. It was evident that the stove's gas valve had been left open. The place was dark and cold. All the windows and curtains were shut, and Antonio was un-bathed and groggy, as though he had been in bed for days.

"What has happened here, Mr. Pontón?" Ms. Chamberlain ran inside the apartment to make sure the stove was off, and she opened the windows to air the place. "How careless could you be? You could have set the building on fire!" she reprimanded him. "You are placing everyone at risk!" she scolded him once again.

"I'm so sorry!" he begged. "I have been sik and have a terrible headache," he said. "I may have forgot turning the stov off," he said, offering a weak explanation.

Mrs. Chamberlain, alarmed, called on her nephew, Douglas Wiger, who also lived in the building, to assist in the matter. Wiger, a needle-thin tall fellow in his mid-twenties, remained in Antonio's apartment while Mrs. Chamberlain and Antonio talked.

Wiger snooped around and noticed a handwritten note with Antonio's signature on the kitchen table. He read it. It was a letter Antonio had written to his classmates. Wiger told his aunt he thought the note was "too flowery" and that he believed that it was meant to be a suicide note. It was filled with farewells and apologetic remarks.

As a result of the frightening incident, Mrs. Chamberlain advised Antonio that she could not run the risk of him hurting himself, the tenants or the building. Sad, but resolute, she told Antonio, "I am sorry my dear, but I have to ask you to move out at once."

. . .

Antonio packed his belongings in his trunk, while Wiger watched him. He left Mrs. Chamberlain's that afternoon. Through a classmate, he was able to rent another apartment from Mrs. Rose Van Guysling at 253 North Pearl Street in Albany. The new apartment was about half-a-mile further away from Albany Law School than his previous apartment, and it was close to the Hudson River.

Mrs. Van Guysling was a nice old lady whose husband's ancestors were long settlers of Schenectady. They were from Zeeland in the Netherlands and had come to America in the 1600's in a ship called "Spotted Cow." Mrs. Van Guysling was in her seventies, wore round glasses and favored flowery prints. She had a strong scent of lavender and was soft spoken, but she was also quite nosy.

One afternoon, Mrs. Van Guysling found Antonio at the mailbox retrieving his mail. She peeked over his shoulder and noticed one of the letters he was carrying was from Bessie Kromer. She asked Antonio, with utmost curiosity, "Is this Bessie your girlfriend?"

He smiled at the inquisitive landlady and replied, "Jehs, madam, we are going to marry soon."

Ms. Van Guysling had seen Antonio carrying a bundle of Bessie's letters when he was leaving the building on one occasion. She thought that Antonio displayed an odd behavior at times, noticed he was often nervous and complained of having headaches.

"Poor Mr. Pontón," she thought to herself. "Law school is not easy."

Ms. Van Guysling offered Antonio medication for his headaches once or twice, feeling pity for his situation.

Although he had fallen behind in his coursework, Antonio continued his studies during the 1913 school year and tried to catch up, aided by the support of the Albany Law School Registrar John C. Watson and by his law school friends.

He also continued to write to Bessie and to receive her letters. From time to time, Antonio and Bessie got together for dinner or a short trip, as they did at the beginning. Although he knew things were changing between them, Antonio hoped their relationship would go

116

back to what it was before.

He knew she still loved him, but there was something interfering with her love.

Chapter 26. The Last Summer

In 1914, Antonio continued his coursework at Albany Law School, and Bessie secured a job teaching grade school at the Lincoln School on Robinson Street in Schenectady, where she was a beloved teacher. Bessie found a cozy apartment in the historic *Conde House*, about four blocks from the school, on 1024 Albany Street. The Conde family descended from the great *Conde of France*. Adam Conde became high constable of Albany in 1724.

On July 1, 1914 Bessie went to New York with her mother to enroll in Columbia University's Summer School. Antonio arrived there the next day. Mrs. Kromer remained with Bessie a week and then returned to Schoharie. Bessie stayed in New York for six weeks total and Antonio stayed with her.

After classes at Columbia ended, Bessie went back to her family home in Schoharie. Antonio followed her back to 27 Main St. with the intention to board there for the rest of the summer. Mrs. Kromer learned from Bessie that Antonio was not doing well in school and was ill. She had also noticed he was nervous and seemed to have constant headaches. Bessie told her mother she was concerned about him and asked her if she could help.

Mrs. Kromer reached out to Reverend Charles M. Karg, pastor of the Schoharie Lutheran Church. Pastor Karg was a laid-back individual with a comforting demeanor. Mrs. Kromer told him what was happening with Antonio and asked the pastor if he could help Antonio with the stress he was facing. The Reverend knew Bessie well, and he had seen Antonio and Bessie together as a couple before.

Reverend Karg noticed that Antonio was discouraged and downhearted. He was under the impression that Mrs. Kromer knew Bessie and Antonio were in a relationship, but that she disapproved. He could see the tension building up between Mrs. Kromer and her daughter over "The Spaniard," Mrs. Kromer's nickname for Antonio.

. . .

As the end of summer approached, prior to returning to her apartment in Schenectady for the school year, Bessie reached out to Antonio to discuss their relationship. They were alone, as Ms. Kromer was at a DAR meeting, and Bessie's brother Charles was at work.

They sat on the porch, where she used to tutor Antonio in English years prior, where he gave her the first rose, where she had fallen in love with him and doodled words of love on his notebook.

"Antonio, I have something important to tell you," she said.

He listened.

"The end of summer is near, and we are going back to our rightful places," she paused. "You, to Albany Law School, and me back to Schenectady to teach." She continued, "You are so dear to me. I have cherished your company for the past three years," she said, looking into his eyes.

She had her hands on her lap, nervously circling her thumbs.

Antonio's heartbeat was accelerating. He was attentive, anticipating that Bessie would declare her love for him, as she had done in previous occasions, and they could marry. He was impatient, and he wanted to take the lead.

"I chare the same feelings with you, Besi," he interrupted her. "I also want to ask somesing important," Antonio revealed in haste. "We have been together for three jears now, like husband and wife. In my mind we're married, but I know this is not official. You deserve the best wedding in the entire world," he said.

Bessie remained speechless, but her eyes began to tear.

"I'm so nervos," he said, pulling out a small box out of his pocket. He opened the box, revealing a ring.

Bessie had never seen such a beautiful jewel.

"Besi. Ju ... You ..." he slowed down, trying to get his words and his pronunciation right. "You are the most beeautifool, intelligent, strong and kind woman I have ever met. There is not a day that I don't spend thinking about you. I miss you terribly. I cannot study because I am thinking of you all the time. I want to spend the rest of my life with you. It would make me the happiest man on Earth if you accept me as your husband," he declared to Bessie. "All I need to do is get your permission to ask your mother for your hand in matrimony," he asked of Bessie.

Bessie was pale, as though she had just seen a ghost.

"Oh, Antonio!" Bessie sighed, frowning with sadness.

He was confused and surprised, expecting an opposite reaction from Bessie, based on her recent promise that she would be true to him.

"Antonio," Bessie said, taking the ring, placing it on the palm of his hand, and closing his fingers onto it. "I feel flattered by your proposal, but ... I must refuse! I can't be your wife!" she continued, "In fact, we should not see each other any longer after we leave here. My mother, well, you know she does not approve. This is why I have been so inconsistent with our relationship. This is driving me insane. I cannot reconcile my love for you and the love and responsibility I have for her," Bessie said.

Antonio was in denial. She could not be rejecting him, after all this time. After all her promises! She led him on to believe.

"Besi, how could you betray me like this?" he said. "Do you love another?" he asked her.

"No, Antonio. It is not that. I just think we are not meant to be together," she said. "I do love you, but I am confused. Everything is against us. The world is against us. My mother ..." she hesitated. "We have behaved like children!"

He could almost hear the words of Nora Kromer speaking through Bessie's mouth. This was Mrs. Kromer speaking, not Bessie.

"Besi, maybe the distans is making you forget your love for me. Maybe you should move closer to Albany so we can be together more," he tried to persuade her.

Bessie looked down silent, as though she was giving consideration to his alternative proposal. She was torn.

"I don't know," she hesitated. "I don't want to move and leave my job. I enjoy it very much," she said. "And I can't leave my mother, either. She has endured so much pain, losing my father and all," she said. "My duty is to her. My loyalty lies with her, first and foremost."

Antonio tried to sway her, "Besi, your mother has your brother Charles. She will not be alone! We can come visit her often. Please don't break up with me! Give me another chance!"

Resolute, she replied, "Antonio, I don't think so. I am sorry. It is better for both of us this way. You need to focus on your studies, and my mother just does not approve. She says it will not work, you being a Spaniard, a Catholic, and all. I just cannot go forward. It is too stressful for my family. People in town are talking. It is stressful for you, also. It is making you fail in school. Our relationship is not good for either of us!"

As a child who has been told he cannot have the toy he wants most, Antonio burst into an angry spell. He went inside the dining room and grabbed the glass vase Etervina had sent as a gift to Mrs. Kromer and Bessie, and he propelled it into the wall. The vase shattered into a million pieces.

Bessie was astonished. She had never seen him behave like this before.

"Antonio!" she raised her voice at him, scolding him.

He turned around and looked at Bessie in the eye with rage and raised his hand as though to hit her. When he realized what he was doing, Antonio stopped at once, looking at the palms of his hand, wondering what on Earth had possessed him. His head was about to explode. The headache was unbearable, and he became sick to his stomach.

Her hands over her face, Bessie began crying.

Antonio brought the palm of his right hand to his forehead, in disbelief of his actions. Then, without a word, he rushed into his bathroom, and Bessie ran out of the house.

He went on to pack his bag.

With tears in his eyes, Antonio walked out the Kromer house, for good.

. . .

Crying, Bessie rushed to see Reverend Karg to share the incident with him, but he was not at the church. She then went looking for her brother Charles at the grocery store. Charles accompanied Bessie back home trying to calm her down.

They saw Antonio had already departed.

That evening, when Mrs. Kromer returned home, Bessie shared with her what had happened. She told her that Antonio asked for her hand in marriage, but that she refused him, even though she still had feelings for him. She explained to her that he did not take rejection well, that he filled with a rage she had never seen before, that he raised his hand at her, looking as a mad man. Bessie told Ms. Kromer that she fell as though Antonio was so angry that he wanted to kill her.

Mrs. Kromer was outraged. She commanded Bessie at once to not see Antonio ever again or correspond with him. The relationship with The Spaniard needed to come to an end, regardless of whether she still had feelings for him or not. His behavior was reprehensible. He was failing in his studies and was sick. His conduct was not normal.

"Bessie, I do not know if his sickness is contagious. And now he has become aggressive, Mrs. Kromer said. "I fear for your welfare. The relationship is over. Do you understand? Over!" she commanded.

. . .

Bessie and Antonio went their separate ways. She returned to Schenectady to prepare for her teaching at the Lincoln School, and he went to Albany to prepare for his studies at Albany Law School. Days after the incident, Bessie received a letter of apology from Antonio.

"Albany, New York. July 3, 1914. Dear Bessie," it read. "I do not know what overcame me. Please forgive me. I love you, and I would never ever hurt you. My world ended upon your rejection. I bought you an engagement ring! I told my parents! You are the only woman I have ever loved with all my heart. Please give our love another chance. I beg you! Yours, Antonio."

Not too long after he wrote his letter to Bessie, Antonio received a response.

"Schenectady, New York. July 14, 1914. Dear Antonio," the letter stated. "This is the most difficult letter I have ever written. Please forget me," it read. "My love for you was lost when you struck me and tried to choke me. Go to your mother and tell her of striking me and of your attempt to kill me," the letter read. "Please do not contact me again," it ended. "Bessie." The letter was written with a shaky handwriting.

"This is not true!" Antonio thought as he read the letter. "Bessie could not say those things about me! I love her! Did I do the things she accuses me of doing in this letter?" he second-guessed his actions.

Confusion set in.

"Did Bessie write such a letter? Am I losing grasp of reality?"

Within seconds, a voice whispered in his ear, "Her mother wrote the letter!"

"Albany, New York. July 20, 1914. Dear Bessie," Antonio wrote. "I cannot believe that your mother is now writing your letters. I did not attempt to kill you. I was angry at your rejection, and I am devastated, but I would never hurt you. I love you! I want to see you! Let's talk, please! Your, Antonio."

"Schenectady, New York. August 3, 1914. Antonio, I do not want to see you again. Please do not write to me. Bessie."

This was the last letter Antonio received from Bessie.

. . .

Antonio's friends tried to console him. Ulpiano Crespo, Eugene Vera, Pedro Beiges and Antonio López visited him at his apartment and insisted he get help.

"Antonio, why don't you return to Puerto Rico for a while, take a break? Distance might help you piece your thoughts back together," Ulpiano Crespo told him. "You can always return to Albany when you have recovered. Mind your health first. You are not well."

"I don't know. If I return without a degree I will be the shame of my family and my people," Antonio said. "I don't want to end up in the *manicomio* (asylum) like the others in mother's family. I want to achieve something before I die, to leave a legacy. At this moment, I am a nobody!"

"But if you are ill, you need to get help. Many ill people recover and go on to live happy and productive lives. You should reconsider. We can all fundraise for your travels back home if you do not wish to impose on your family," Vera said.

Antonio sighed.

"You are in no shape to continue studying. Law school is very stressful. You have to be in the right mindset, and you are not. And your girlfriend, Bessie, she is contributing in great measure to your troubles. She is not favorable for you! One day she welcomes you, the next day she refuses you. You must place distance between you two. You cannot continue living this life. It will not end well, and you know it!" López said.

Silence.

"Well, you know where to find us if you need us. You are not alone, Antonio. You have friends who care for you," Beiges said, as they left.

Sleep buried his desperation.

. . .

He woke up to knocks on his door.
"Just a minute!" he said out loud. "I'm coming!"
He got up and straightened himself as he opened the door.
"Besi!" he said, overcome with emotion.
He held her and never let go.

Chapter 27. A Perfect Storm

"**M**other, I still love him! I am torn as to what to do," Bessie said. "You are asking me to do the impossible!"

Mrs. Kromer was furious. After she sent the last letter "from Bessie," Mrs. Kromer made it clear to her daughter that she did not want Antonio near her.

"Bessie, this relationship is trouble for you. The Spaniard is not the man for you. You must be strong," Mrs. Kromer said to her daughter. "You have no other recourse."

Bessie remained silent.

"Have you been seeing him again?"

Silence.

"Bessie Kromer, have you been seeing The Spaniard again?"

Bessie broke down into sobs.

Mrs. Kromer's eyes were on fire. She knew her daughter. She knew Bessie was concealing the continued affair from her. She needed to do something more drastic than forcing her daughter to send the letters ending the relationship. These were not doing the deed. She had to halt any chance that their relationship would resume.

Mrs. Kromer retained an attorney, Mr. Dugan, to place a restraining order on Antonio and to file a police report that Antonio had threatened Bessie. She also relayed to the police that Antonio had a revolver.

. . .

Antonio was in *Constitutional Law* class when officer Hiram Walker and another officer, of the Albany District Attorney's Office, came to arrest him, interrupting the lecture.

"How can I help you gentlemen?" said Professor Lewis R. Parker as the officers entered the classroom with Mr. Watson.

"Mr. Antonio Pontón?" said Officer Walker, addressing the class.

"Jehs," he stood up, startled. "I am Antonio Pontón," he said with wide-open eyes as he looked at his professor, Watson and the officers.

"We would like you to accompany us to police headquarters, please," Walker said.

The students chattered in the background. Professor Parker was in awe. Watson remained silent and appeared saddened by the occurrence.

"But, why?" Antonio said. "What is the matter, sir?"

"There has been a report filed against you, sir. We will explain. Please come with us," said Walker.

"Jehs, sir."

Antonio picked up his papers and placed them in his bag. As he approached the classroom door, Walker took Antonio's bag, gave it to the accompanying officer and handcuffed the student in front of everyone. An embarrassed Antonio walked out of the classroom, escorted by the police officers and Mr. Watson.

. . .

"Mr. Pontón," said officer Walker, standing up before Antonio in the interrogating room. "Do you own a revolver?"

"No, sir. I don't," Antonio said, sitting in the uncomfortable chair, while squinting his eyes at the bright light above him in an attempt to make eye contact with Walker.

"Then you would not mind if we search your person?" the officer said.

"No, sir, you can search me. You will find nothing of the sort."

Walker and another officer searched Antonio and did not find the weapon Mrs. Kromer alleged he had.

"Mr. Pontón, do you mind if we search your apartment?" Walker asked.

"Why?" Antonio said.

"To see if you have a revolver there," the officer responded.

"Ju won't find a gun in my apartment," Antonio said. "I don't own a revolver!"

The officer paused.

"I don't want any trouble, so if I let you see my apartment would you release me?" asked Antonio. I have a great deal of homework, and

I need to prepare for tomorrow's classes."

"Sure. If there is no gun, Mr. Pontón, you will be released, but you need to understand there is also a restraining order against you. You cannot approach Miss Bessie Kromer," the officer said.

"She filed a restraining order?" Antonio said. "Why would she do that?"

"Her mother was with her. She hired a lawyer to file the order. Her mother said you tried to kill Miss Kromer. Miss Kromer admitted you threatened her this past summer."

"That is not true!" Antonio said.

"Well, there will be a hearing and you can talk to the judge about that," Walker said.

"We argued, like couples argue. I was bery angry at her, but I would not hurt her," Antonio said. "I love her!"

"Well, we have a restraining order," the officer said.

"Her mother says I tried to kill Besi, but if you ask Besi without her mother present, she will tell ju the truth. I got angry because she broke up with me, after she had said she would be true to me," Antonio said. "But her mother is forcing her. She doesn't want us together because I am Puerto Rican. But Besi wants to be with me. She came to see me after we argued!" he said.

"Mr. Pontón," Walker said. "The truth will come out in court. It always does. You should know. You are a law student! You should believe in the American Justice System. It is the best in the world! If you are innocent, you will be set free!"

"Okay," said Antonio. "Well, I am innocent. Let's go to my apartment. Ju will see. I have no revolver. Mrs. Kromer is lying!"

. . .

The officers accompanied Antonio to his apartment, which they searched, but they could not find a revolver there, either. However, they did find a set of brass knuckles inside a locked trunk, after they asked Antonio to open it for them.

"Looky here!" Walker said to the accompanying officer. "We struck gold!"

"Shiny brass knuckles!" the officer said.

"Jehs, I brought them from Puerto Rico when I came hear the summer of 1911," said Antonio. "It was a gift from my oldest brother.

Is there anything wron with that? It's not a gun!"

Possession of brass knuckles was sufficient to support a charge under the *New York Sullivan Act*. The gun control law was enacted in New York State on August 31, 1911, a couple of months after Antonio's arrival to Schoharie. The law required New Yorkers to secure a license to possess concealed firearms. Unlicensed possession could result in a misdemeanor, and carrying the unlicensed weapon was a felony. The law extended to punish as a felony the unlicensed possession or carrying of other weapons, such as brass knuckles, sandbags, blackjacks, bludgeons, bombs, a dagger, "dangerous knife" or razor *"with intent to use the same unlawfully."*

Some people questioned the constitutionality of the act under the Second Amendment of the United States Constitution. Many believed the law was enacted to discriminate against immigrants in New York, as it was passed on a wave of anti-immigrant rhetoric as a measure to disarm an alleged criminal element. The police had all discretion to grant the licenses and could arbitrarily discriminate against "undesirable elements." About 70 percent of the arrests made under the law when enacted were of immigrants. The law is still being questioned today as biased towards licensing the wealthy.

"Mr. Pontón, the Sullivan Law requires a license for possession of brass knuckles," the officer said. "Do you have a permit to have these, sir?"

"Officer Walker, I did not know of the Sullivan Law," Antonio said. "I brought the knuckles from Puerto Rico for self-protection. I heard of the many issues with crime in New York. It is customary for men to have brass knuckles in Puerto Rico. My brother gave these to me, and I did not know I needed to get a permit for the knuckles when I came to New York. In any case, I have them stored in my locked trunk and never carry them with me. I have no ill intentions to use them!"

His explanation did not persuade the officers.

"Mr. Pontón, you are under arrest for the illegal possession of a weapon, under the Sullivan Act," said Walker. "You are also under arrest for threatening Miss Bessie Kromer."

. . .

Antonio was taken back to police headquarters, where he was arraigned. His bail was set at $500.

"Are you going to post bail, Mr. Pontón?" asked the court officer.

"I don't have that much money on my person, sir," Antonio responded. "I will have to call my father. He is going to kill me!"

"Well, you will have to go to jail until you can post your bail, Mr. Pontón," the officer said.

"I have never been in jail before!" Antonio said, turning to Walker. "Please do not put me in jail!"

"Many thugs have not been in jail until they get caught, Mr. Pontón. You got caught, so you are going to jail," said Walker.

"But I am not a criminal!" said Antonio. "I am not a criminal!"

"You can phone your father if you wish, Mr. Pontón," said Walker.

. . .

After receiving the call from his son, Manuel was devastated. He retained a New York attorney who had approached Antonio after learning about his arrest, Mr. Lewis Cass. The lawyer posted the excessive bail of $500 the next day and got Antonio released.

To further his embarrassment, the local newspaper immediately published the news about Antonio's arrest. The paper got its facts wrong and stated that he had been arrested for possession of a revolver. Other papers mentioned the brass knuckles. Antonio was humiliated and angry.

"Mr. Pontón, I will be in touch regarding this matter. Just go home and get some rest. We will get all this sorted out. I will contact you. We will meet again," said Cass. "It is obvious that you were set up by your girlfriend's mother. We will fix this! Just stay away from the girl, do you understand?"

"I will," Antonio said in a daze.

He went back to his apartment as directed by his lawyer.

. . .

As Antonio arrived to his apartment, there was a note on his door from Mr. Watson, the Albany Law School Registrar, with a message informing him that he was not welcome at the school until the arrest matter was resolved.

Antonio arranged for a meeting with Dean J. Newton Fiero and attended the meeting with Mr. Cass to discuss his situation and petition to be readmitted to school while the legal matters settled.

During the meeting, Dean Fiero stated to both men that because of the situation with Bessie and the Sullivan Act arrest, Antonio "had broken one of the five rules" required for a student to remain at Albany Law School. He would not be welcome back at the school, for good.

Antonio had been expelled.

. . .

"How could this be?" asked Antonio as he left the university with his attorney. "Isn't a man innocent until proven guilty? This is a person's word against another. The knuckles, everyone has these back home in Puerto Rico! It's like a toy! When I came to New York, they were not illegal hear! How was I supposed to kno? They've been in my trunk ever sins I arrive hear. I have not even tek them out once! How can I be punished like thees?"

"Mr. Pontón," said Cass. "As a law student, you know the maxim *'ignorantia juris non excusat.'* Ignorance of the law is no excuse. I know you are new to this country, but the law is the law. In any case, we will take care of this. You stay put. I will talk to your father, and we will help you get out of this mess! He needs to send me some money first, so I can represent you in this matter. I don't work for free! We will take it from there. I will let you know."

. . .

Back in his apartment, Antonio became desperate. Sitting on his bed in the darkness, his hands on his face, his elbows resting on his knees, he tried to convince himself that his situation was all a nightmare.

"This is not real. I am dreaming this!"

"All prospects for a career in law have ended for you, Antonio," a voice said to him. "Your efforts were meaningless," another voice interjected.

"You reputation is forever tarnished," a third voice jabbed. "You've lost the love of your life," another pierced his heart.

"You wasted your father's money," the voices kept going. "All your dreams are now crushed. You have tainted your family's good name!"

"Worst of all, you cannot have her!" the voices mocked him with laughter. "You are good for nothing!"

He could not make them stop.

"Shut up! Shut up!" he cried inconsolably while covering his ears, shaking his head left and right. "Stop, already! Have mercy on me! Please God, have mercy on me! Help me!" he pleaded.

As he lay on his bed crying, he covered his head with his pillow in a failed attempt to silence the voices taunting him.

His mind was forsaking him.

"How will you face your mother and father?" the voices started again. "How will you face the rest of your family? How will you face your friends? How will you go on?"

The voices pounded the walls of his mind as he tried to sleep. They would not cease.

He got up, went to the kitchen and poured a full glass of cognac, which he drank as though it was water.

In and out of his frantic state, exhausted and under the influence of the alcohol, Antonio managed to pass out.

. . .

When he opened his eyes, he could barely see. It was dark, but there was moonlight. It was a clear night. He could see the sky peppered with stars. His head pounded.

"I must be hungover," he thought.

He heard a crackling sound. He sat up and scanned around, realizing that the crackle's source was a burning fire close to where he was laying.

"Where am I?"

There were mountains, but he was not in New York.

"What the? ... Are these *coquí* sounds?" The high-pitch of the frog's chant was louder than usual.

"Am I back in Comerío?"

"But why am I here?" he asked out loud. "How did I get here?"

He heard footsteps. Soon after, the large silhouette of a man approached him. As the silhouette walked past the fire and got closer to Antonio, it became smaller. Still sitting on the ground, he looked up to unveil the identity of the man, but the glare of the moon did not allow him to see his face.

131

"Who are you?" Antonio asked.

"*¡Eres la vergüenza de la familia!* You are the shame of our family!" the faceless man said. "How could you do this to us?"

Antonio recognized the voice of his father Manuel.

"*¡Padre!* Father!" he said. "Is that you? I can no longer tell reality from fiction! I am so afraid!"

"Afraid? Your mother and I gave you everything a man could ever need or want! All you had to do was sit down and study! That's all you had to do! No manual labor under the sun. You just had to sit down, and learn! But you failed, even at that!" the voice said.

"Father, I tried. I really tried! I worked hard! My mind ... It is failing me! I have terrible headaches. I can't focus or memorize anything! ... It was her mother's fault! Her mother made up a story to break us up!

Silence.

"Please give me another chance! I will see a doctor! I will get to the bottom of this!" Antonio pleaded to the man. "I am a Pontón! I will conquer this!"

"A Pontón?" said the voice. "You don't even come close to what I have passed through, or what your brothers have endured! All the sacrifice! A Pontón? Pontón men are hardworking! Pontón men have character! They have values!"

Antonio saw the man walk towards the fire. From it, he pulled an iron rod like those his father used to brand the family's cattle. The silhouette approached him with the iron rod. Antonio could see the incandescent letter P growing bigger as the faceless man got near him.

"A Pontón?" the man repeated, approaching Antonio closer.

"No! Father!" Antonio pleaded. "No!"

"You are not a Pontón! You don't have Pontón in you!" the man screamed at Antonio, as he branded him above his right ankle with the hot iron.

Antonio screamed in anguish at the pain of the burning iron on his leg, which the man applied with such force that the incandescent metal ate through the fabric of his pants and through his skin, burning him almost to the bone.

He could smell his charred flesh.

"You will look at the letter P burned on your leg for the rest of your life! It will remind you that you have failed! You are no longer a Pontón! You are no longer part of this family!"

Antonio's heart was pounding. His shivers turned into sweat. The sweat coming down his forehead caught up with the tears running down his cheeks.

The pain. The hurt. The shame.

There were no words he could think or say. Nothing he could do.

As the faceless man completed his deed, he turned and walked away, threw the iron back into the fire and vanished into the darkness.

"Father! Father!" Antonio cried, as he lay hurt on the ground.

There was dead silence in return, but for the sounds of a *múcaro* (screech-owl) that flew away, startled by Antonio's screams.

Antonio opened his eyes to realize that it was all a nightmare. He looked at his ankle. There was nothing. No signs of a burn, nor a letter P, nothing.

He could still taste the cognac in his dry mouth.

The voices awakened with him.

"Life is no longer worth living," they assured him.

Chapter 28. Erasing Antonio

"Schoharie, September 25, 1914. My Dear Bessie, I hope this letter finds you well," wrote Nora Kromer to her daughter. "I am enclosing a cutting from the newspaper, describing The Spaniard as his true self. He was arrested for possession of an unlawful weapon. God only knows what he was planning to do with it, maybe even hurt you! I know that you have been seeing him for a long time, Bessie, and that you traveled with him as husband and wife. I am writing to plead with you to end your affair with The Spaniard, for your own sake and for that of your folk. Please erase him from your heart and from your mind. He is trouble! Love, Mother."

Mrs. Kromer hoped that her daughter stayed away from Antonio, for good. She thought that having him arrested would do the trick, once and for all.

But she was terribly mistaken.

Mrs. Kromer's plan to split the couple brought about the desired separation in the most horrendous of ways.

Chapter 29. Love is the Blame for It

Around the third week of September of 1914, Antonio entered the *Albany Hardware Company* to purchase a hunting knife. Store clerk J. J. Cullen tended to him. Because the new *Sullivan Law of New York of 1911* imposed a three-day cooling off period before a person could retrieve a purchased weapon, Antonio completed a questionnaire that asked for general information, including any history of mental illness and prior arrests and convictions. He began to fill the questionnaire, ignored the mental illness and criminal history sections, and on the third day, he went back to pick up the knife. Then, he returned to his apartment on 148 North Pearl Street and began writing.

"My Dear Mr. Watson,

By the next mail I shall get $100 from home, and I want you to do for me a last favor. I want you to pay it as follows: For yourself, $20; Thompson and Hare, $6.05: at the armory, $12.50; Mrs. Halsey, $4.10; total, $42.65.

With the other money I want you to pay all the expense of my burial, and if there is not sufficient money then notify my people of the amount necessary if you use any of your own money to pay off everything.

Pardon me for this resolution, but it was necessary for me to do it. I know that this will be a disgrace that I bring to my people, but I cannot help it. Love is the blame for it.

I go in peace. I hope you and my countrymen will pray for me. Good-bye, good-bye all.

Yours, who was your friend,

Antonio Pontón

Albany Law School, Albany, N. Y.

Excuse all mistakes, but I am very nervous."

Antonio placed his letter to Watson in his pocket, along with other letters he wrote to his parents asking for forgiveness and saying his farewells. But he needed to see Bessie one last time before he departed Earth for good.

On Friday, October 2, 1914, Antonio boarded the streetcar and went to Schenectady to see her. He paced up and down her street, but there were no signs of Bessie. He then realized that she might still be at work.

He took the streetcar once again, got off at the Robinson Street stop and waited for her to come out of the Lincoln School.

Chapter 30. At the Corner of Albany and Backus

B essie had just returned to the Lincoln School from spending the day with her young students on a field trip. It was a long day, but they were all in good spirits. When all the students left, Bessie emerged from the main door of the school building.

"Antonio, you should not be here!" Her heart froze at the sight of him.

"I needed to see you, Besi," he said. "One last time."

She agreed to walk together to *O. J. Eckerson*, the grocery store on 1002 Albany Street.

"I can't live without you, Besi," he said.

"I know, Antonio, but there is no use!" she responded. "You are making this harder on both of us!"

At the store, Antonio and Bessie engaged in a heated argument.

"Please, Besi!" he begged her to get back together.

"It's no use, no use!" she stated, upon his persistent appeals.

Onlookers noticed the couple arguing.

Upset, Bessie paid for her groceries and walked out of the store, Antonio following her.

The voices in Antonio's head got louder and more agitated.

"Go after her, make her take you back!" the voices instructed.

It was 6:35 p.m.

Antonio walked behind Bessie trying to catch up with her near the corner of Albany and Backus. She continued to walk at a faster pace, ignoring him.

"Go on, Antonio, stop her from leaving!" the voices got louder.

"Please go home, Antonio!" she begged him. She hated hurting him, but this was something she had to do.

Antonio was desperate. He caught up with her and stood in front of her, blocking her way.

"Show her how much it hurts! Show her!" the voices overcame him.

He pulled out the hunting knife.

"Let me be!" Antonio screamed at the voices. "Please, I beg you!"

He stood in front of her, pointing the knife at his chest. Trembling. Sweating bullets. He wanted Bessie to feel the pain he suffered. He wanted her to see him die. She had taken his life already. He just had to finish it.

"Just finish it!" the voices insisted. "Set yourself free!"

He was in a trance. She was petrified.

"Good-bye, Besi. I loved you more than my own life," he said, hopeless, tears down his cheeks.

It was the end of it all.

She remained standing there, frozen by fear. Their entire relationship flashed before her eyes. The first glance at him when he came through the door at 27 Main Street that July of 1911, the lessons, his *piropos*, the first rose, the first dream, the parks, the monuments, Coney Island, New York City, Saratoga Springs, the hotels, his touch, their passionate lovemaking, their separations, the reconciliations, the laughter, the tears, her mother, the final breakup, the pain, the fear.

It felt like years, but it was milliseconds.

Soon after, people amassed on the street at the sound of repeated female screams, followed by dead silence.

. . .

Sergeant C. F. A. Engel, an officer from the Schenectady police, happened to be walking by with his police dog. He saw Antonio striking Bessie and rushed to the scene. He saw that Bessie had collapsed on the street and lay lifeless, in a pool of blood. Antonio began retreating at the sight of Sergeant Engel running towards him with his police dog. Engel ran after Antonio in an attempt to detain him, commanding his dog to assist.

Antonio stopped, the dog biting him, and just before Sergeant Engel's own eyes, Antonio stabbed himself in the chest three times, collapsing to the ground.

Chapter 31. Headlines and Accounts

Dramatic coverage of the incident was immediate, with many press and police interviews taking place at the scene, and headlines appearing the next day of the events, Saturday, October 3, 1914. The crime's headlines shared the front page of the paper along with the latest news about the European War, the preamble to World War I.

The headline in the *Schenectady Gazette* on October 3, 1914 read:

"BESSIE S. KROMER SLAIN AT ALBANY AND BACKUS STREET LAST NIGHT BY ANTONIO PONTON, A FORMER STUDENT AT THE ALBANY LAW SCHOOL-SLAYER PROBABLY DYING AT THE HOSPITAL. PONTON AFTER STABBING THE GIRL FIFTEEN TIMES ATTEMPTS SUICIDE"

The coverage featured a detailed account of events, including Sergeant Engel's statement to the *Schenectady Gazette*. Engel stated to the reporter: "I heard the scream of a woman, and I looked up to see where it came from. Up the street, a distance of about 150 yards, I saw a man and a woman standing at the curb. As I looked, the man raised his right hand and struck two blows at the left breast of the woman. She started into the street, the man started into the street, and I ran toward them. Just as I was within three feet of the man, he struck himself with the knife and my hand was on him as he fell. He said nothing but pointed to his trouser pocket. I searched him to see if he had a revolver or other weapon and in the meantime a call was sent for the patrol wagon, in which he was taken to the Ellis Hospital. The woman took a step or two into the street and fell. They were in front of 1002 Albany Street, the grocery store, when I saw him strike her. He fell about in front of 1000 Albany Street, close to Backus Street."

The press reported a crowd of about one thousand strong piled up in the area, curious to learn details about what had happened. The police blocked and secured the two bodies to ensure they were not tampered with. The mass of people on the street impaired the traffic, and the scene was chaotic.

Police found the following items on Antonio's body:

A pawn ticket showing he had secured $30 for a pocket watch and $10 for an engagement ring and a watch chain. He also had in his possession the newspaper clipping documenting his arrest the previous week, a letter addressed to his father, Manuel Pontón, Comerío, Puerto Rico, and $8.26 in change.

Antonio was also carrying a letter dated September 28, 1914. The letter was from 148 North Pearl Street, Albany, to Bessie Kromer, written in pencil on a torn page from a school composition book and was signed by Antonio Pontón. It read:

"My Darling Bessie, I am writing this letter to you, even though I know you are not going to reply. But I do want you to write back. Just write something back to me. I know that one day you'll regret breaking my heart. But I will forgive you. I wish that I might be like you, but God knows I cannot. I want to see you again. Maybe after work? I miss your voice. It will mean so much to me to see you again."

Antonio had other letters on his person. In addition to the one to his parents in Spanish, he carried the letter to the Albany Law School Registrar, Mr. Watson, asking him to dispose of his debts. The writing to his parents was peppered with *"Adiós"* and other words of farewell, such as "farewell forever," and allusions of regret and the disgrace he was bringing to his family. "My death will be painful at first, but it will bring more stability to the family and lift a burden off your shoulders," he wrote. "I have been a burden to you all. It is best this way." It was written while he was crying, as teardrops had smeared some of the ink on the letter.

Police found the following items on Bessie's body:

A pocketbook stained with blood, containing a house key, a list of names of children and their addresses, and $4.39 in cash.

Coroner E. Holcomb Jackson searched Bessie's and Antonio's apartments. He secured letters written by Mrs. Kromer to Bessie, containing statements where Mrs. Kromer was pleading that she "end her affair with The Spaniard, for her own sake and for that of her folk." The letters also indicated that Mrs. Kromer was aware of the relationship between Antonio and Bessie for some time, and that she knew they were acting as husband and wife, that they were traveling together and staying at hotels. The police also recovered a photograph of Antonio and Bessie together. It was taken at a resort, showing them standing on what seemed to be the rear platform of a passenger coach.

. . .

Antonio Pontón, now addressed as "the former law student turned murderer," was taken to *Ellis Hospital* in Schenectady, New York in critical condition. During his suicide attempt, he managed to pierce one of his lungs, was bleeding profusely, and was expected to die. The press surrounded the hospital hoping that they could secure an interview with Antonio, if and when he regained consciousness.

Bessie's injuries were multiple and severe. Antonio stabbed her 15 times. She had a deep gash on her right cheekbone; her heart, liver and lung were punctured; and her right arm slashed and nearly severed, the wound caused when she was turning in a desperate act to run away from him. Bessie died in an instant.

Bessie's mother and brother Charles came to Schenectady the evening of Bessie's death. They took her back home to Schoharie Saturday afternoon. She was buried next to her father Charles, at the St. Paul Lutheran Cemetery.

Chapter 32. In Faltering English

"Mr. Pontón, you rest now, you understand? You have lost much blood and your wounds are severe," said the nurse to Antonio. It was about an hour-and-a-half after he had arrived into Ellis Hospital's emergency room on October 2nd.

Antonio nodded.

He was disoriented and still in and out of consciousness. He had been subject to critical surgery for his wounds. He had a collapsed lung and a wound that almost pierced his heart.

He fell asleep.

After the nurse left the room, Bernie J. Waterman, a reporter for the *Schenectady Gazette* sneaked into Antonio's room and captured the only statement made by Antonio regarding the matter. The two men were alone in the hospital room.

The paper published Waterman's version of Antonio's words the next day, October 3rd, stating that Antonio made the statement "in faltering English, from his hospital deathbed."

"Antonio Ponton's Statement"

"About three years ago my father sent me to this country to go to a college to get an education in medicine or law. I choose to study law. When I came over here I was unable to speak the English language. I went to the country in Schoharie County to take English lessons and stayed in Schoharie town one year and two months.

I stopped at the house of Bessie S. Kromer in Schoharie for one year and two months and paid her mother $7 a week for board and room. The girl began to make love to me, writing in my books, 'Yo te amo' (I love you) in Spanish, and telling me everything concerning love, in Spanish, as she was able to speak that language. Then I started to make love to her.

About two years ago she came to Schenectady to teach in the

Lincoln School - and she said to me 'Go to Albany Law School, as Albany and Schenectady are near to each other and in that way we can see each other very often.' I called on her three or four times a week.

About a year ago I had trouble with her, and I thought myself 'it was better for me to go away' to another state to go to another college, and I wrote to Harvard for my entrance blanks.

When she knew this fact she did not let me go and told me to stay in Albany and not to go away. Then I stopped my going and remained in Albany just to please her. It seems two years ago until two weeks ago, we were together all the time, going from one place to another, as Albany, Troy, Saratoga Springs, Johnstown, Fonda, New York City and Coney Island, and Schenectady, going from one hotel to another as husband and wife. Two weeks ago we went to Saratoga Springs. We registered at the American Hotel by the name of Mr. and Mrs. Fernandez and after stopping we went to a show, getting back to Schenectady at 11:15 o'clock. I took her home at 11:30 o'clock.

On the road she swore to be true to me as long as we lived and said to me: 'Never mind what my mother says and never mind what may happen between us. I will always love you.' And then I promised her just the same, to give up everything for her. This same night I gave her gifts that my mother sent her by me, and a picture of mine. Last week Saturday afternoon I got her last letter and she wrote me as ever: a nice letter.

The same day she went with her mother over to Albany to see a lawyer, Mr. Dugan, to make me stop from coming over to see her, to stop me from writing to her, and not to care any more for her, she making a complaint against me that I was carrying a gun, and the district attorney's assistant sent a fellow to my school where I was attending the lectures.

I came down with the fellow and went to see the district attorney, who asked me if I was carrying a gun and I said I was not. Then the district attorney came with me to my room and found in my trunk a brass knuckle, which I did not know was prohibited in this country, having had it in my possession for six years but I never carried that with me nor used it for any purpose.

Afterward he took me to the police court to answer to the complaint. Having been sent to jail, I could not get bail and remained in jail one day. Afterward when I was out, the secretary of the Albany Law School told me that I could not attend the school until the case was over. This morning I went with Mr. Cass, who is a lawyer, and knows my father, who when he read in the paper of my trouble was sorry for me, to the school, and this lawyer was talking with the dean of the school about me and about my father. The dean told him I could not go any more to the school for all these troubles with the girl.

Then I found myself sorry because of the reason that my father sent me over to this country to go to a college, spending about $3,000 on me. When I found out the girl was deceiving me, believing that she was true, fair and honest, and being all the things contrary, then I felt ashamed, because she was telling me she cared for me when she did not. Then I thought of taking a step, which I hope God and my family and friends will forgive me. I did it also for having been in the jail, where I had never been in my life before, being a disgrace for my family and for myself.

I hope that my friend Mr. Karg from Schoharie, will write to my people, and at the same time forgive me for what I have done and pray for me."

During Waterman's inquiry, Antonio was dazed and in and out of consciousness, and he did not have the opportunity to seek legal counsel to protect himself from what was about to come.

Chapter 33. Schenectady Jail

Coroner E. H. Jackson waited on the outcome of Antonio's injuries before holding an inquest. His injuries were severe enough that doctors had given up all hope for Antonio's survival. However, to their surprise, he recovered, and it was not long before he was transported to the Schenectady Jail to await trial.

Sheriff Louis A. Welch supervised the Schenectady Jail, assisted by a matron, Mrs. Welch, two jailers and an undersheriff, Mr. Russell R. Hunt.

"Good day, Mr. Pontón," said the Sheriff. "I am Sheriff Louis Welch."

"Good day, Cheriff Welch," said Antonio.

Sheriff Welch's overall presence was somewhat comforting. Welch was a heavy-set man with broad shoulders and a soft crinkle between his eyebrows. His brown hair was short on the sides, but longer on top, parted on the left and combed over, making two soft u-shaped curves above his forehead, one bigger than the other, which he held in place with *Brilliantine*. Welch also had a bushy moustache showing signs of gray. It spread about three to four inches to each side and overlapped a portion of his upper lip.

"How do you like the new facilities, Mr. Pontón?" said the Sheriff, making some conversation with the new inmate.

"Well, I don't kno yet, Cheriff," said Antonio, who had just come from a hospital room ten times better than his new quarters.

"Please let the officers know if you need anything, Mr. Pontón. There are rules to follow, you know. There is a time to get up, a time to eat, a time to shower, and a time to go to sleep. This is a jail, after all. But we treat our prisoners with respect, and we expect the same treatment in return," said Welch.

"Jessir," said Antonio.

The Schenectady Jail was now located in a new facility at 320

Veeder Avenue. It contained 88 cells inside a four-story brick structure built behind the Sheriff's residence. It had a jail yard on the west end, and it was exposed on three sides. There was a doorway in the north part of the yard, which opened into the yard of the courthouse. Its basement contained bathroom facilities and a passageway connecting to the Sheriff's residence. Undersheriff Hunt's sleeping quarters were right next to the prisoner's cells, in a separate room.

The first floor had a steel cellblock with two parallel rows of ten cells each, divided by a utility corridor. Inside Antonio's 8 feet long x 6 feet wide x 8 feet high cell there were an iron-hinged bed, a sink and a water closet, which showed signs of premature staining. The cell's doors worked on the slide system with a central control lock on one end. The electric lights were located through the door's iron bars, outside of the cell. There was a shower-bath compartment on the west end of the cell rows. The heating system was by steam pipes and extended along the sidewalls. The cold cell floor was made of red concrete.

The second, third and fourth floors of the jail were just like the first. The top floor above the Sheriff's residence housed two hospital rooms and two rows of four cells each, separated by a corridor, geared to house juveniles and females, held separate from the adult males and each other.

Antonio, as other prisoners, had his own soap and towel. His bed had a mattress, bed sheets, a pillow and a pillowcase. He was housed with the other prisoners awaiting trial, separate from those already sentenced. For this reason, he was not assigned to labor. The regular prisoners ate two meals a day, breakfast at 8:00 a.m. and lunch/dinner at 2:00 p.m., except when they were assigned to assist the prison chef in the kitchen or to the prison cleaning crew, in which case they ate three meals a day. When not working in the kitchen or cleaning, prisoners labored on road building projects, crushing stone, and other jobs.

. . .

"No, sankju," Antonio told the officer, who had just brought him breakfast.

He had no appetite and refused to eat much of anything the first-week he was there. He did drink some water and slept most of the time.

The Sheriff and his wife were concerned about Antonio's health. He was still recovering from his self-inflicted wounds, and his mental illness was evident. They had to insist he eat his meals and stay put for his upcoming trial.

On one occasion, Sheriff Welch took it upon himself to drive Antonio around town, just to get him to break out of his melancholic behavior. When questioned by others about this "irresponsible" practice, the Sheriff stated that Antonio had fallen into a depressed state and "he needed some fresh air" or else, he was sure to die and escape the hand of justice.

Sometimes, Sheriff Welch would have a meal or two with Antonio to see if he could get him out of his depression.

"Escuse me Cheriff, you've got somethin in your mohstach," said Antonio.

"Thank you, Mr. Pontón. And there will probably be more after dessert!" the Sheriff responded, smiling, while wiping his moustache.

Antonio chuckled.

The Sheriff made Antonio feel that his life mattered, even under his saddening circumstances. He made him hopeful.

Many did not agree with the compassion the Sheriff displayed towards inmates, but most prisoners appreciated that he treated them as human beings. Welch stressed that compassion and the rigor of prison discipline were not mutually exclusive.

A member of the Socialist Party of New York, Sheriff Welch was an avid advocate of prison reform and appeared to be a man who had the best interests of his prisoners at heart. He suggested various improvements to the jailhouse, including that an iron and an ironing board be provided, so that a prisoner would press their clothes upon discharge.

"It is difficult for a man to secure employment with his clothes all in creases," the Sheriff once wrote in a request to the New York State Commission of Prisons.

Antonio grew fond of Sheriff Welch for the months he was in the Schenectady Jail. The Sheriff and his wife showed humanity towards Antonio, clearly a lost soul amid the prisoner population.

Chapter 34. Conjectures

During the week following Antonio Pontón's crime, reporters' stories poured into the newspapers with speculative renditions about Antonio, his family, and how "his wealthy father of noble origin" would do anything to save his son from a fatal fate.

On October 7, 1914, the *Amsterdam Daily Democrat and Recorder* reported:

"No expense will be spared in defending Antonio Ponton, the Porto Rican law student to be tried for the slaying in Schenectady last week of Bessie Kromer ... a grade school teacher. It was reported Tuesday, when news of a message from Ponton's father to Lewis Cass, counsel for the student, was made known, telling the lawyer the slayer's parents will back their son with their wealth."

Yet on December 5, 1914, the same paper published an apparent change of heart by Manuel. Its headline read, "Ponton is Disowned by his Rich Father." The paper stated that "Lewis Cass, an Albany attorney who was retained by Ponton at the time of the inquest in the case, announced yesterday that Ponton's father, said to be a wealthy Porto Rican planter, had written that he would supply no money for his son's defense because of the latter's many escapades, and that he had disowned Antonio."

The paper reported that Etervina had attempted to persuade Cass to help her son, that she "wrote Mr. Cass a letter in which she said her husband had not relented and would send no money for the defense of his son, but she pleaded with the attorney to save her boy."

Mr. Cass was leveraging Antonio's situation for self-gain, and Manuel had no other choice than to fire him. Upset about his discharge, the lawyer announced in public that he had resigned because "he was not going to work for free," when in fact he had been collecting excessive amounts of money from the Pontón family to represent Antonio ever since Mrs. Kromer had him arrested. The attorney's public representations about the case were most unethical, lacked sensitivity and showed poor professionalism.

The price tag for Antonio's defense was daunting. Aside from the initial $500 bail Manuel had to post on behalf of his son, an amount that at that time could support the purchase of a house or the wages of enough labor force to plant tobacco for a whole year for a small farm, Manuel had been paying everything Cass demanded for months.

Cash flow was tight. Manuel had already mortgaged his properties to support Antonio's education, living expenses, legal fees to date, and the tobacco farming operations. His land was valued between $16,000 and $17,000, and he did not have much equity left to secure another mortgage to hire additional legal counsel, sustain the harvest, pay his workers and support all the families on his land. He had to buy time to sell the year's tobacco. There was so much at stake, not only his son. To make matters worse, Manuel's health was also failing.

For Manuel, who was already in his sixties, the task of defending his son Antonio in a foreign land was universes apart from the challenges he confronted when he migrated to Puerto Rico as a child. He was not 14 years old any longer. He knew that he could not endure this arduous journey alone, as he did the first.

Manuel's advisors in Puerto Rico urged him that time was of the essence. After Cass cashed in and walked out, Antonio was left without legal representation at a critical time. The quickest course of action to ensure that Antonio had a lawyer during his indictment was to secure representation by public defenders. If the verdict were not favorable, Antonio would be entitled to an appeal. By the time the trial ended, the tobacco harvest would be over and Manuel would have the funds to secure private counsel, if still needed.

Manuel trusted his advisors. He consented to public defenders taking over Antonio's case. The new attorneys denied the report that Antonio's relatives had disowned him and began to prepare their case.

Antonio had no visitors at the jail, except for his attorneys, and he received no mail. He communicated with his family through his lawyers, who left some belated Christmas gifts for him from his family in Puerto Rico.

Part IV. The Trial

"No person ... shall be compelled in any criminal case to be a witness against himself, nor be deprived of life, liberty, or property, without due process of law ..."
- Fifth Amendment, United States Constitution

"In all criminal prosecutions, the accused shall enjoy the right to a speedy and public trial, by an impartial jury of the State and district wherein the crime shall have been committed, which district shall have been previously ascertained by law, and to be informed of the nature and cause of the accusation; to be confronted with the witnesses against him; to have compulsory process for obtaining witnesses in his favor, and to have the Assistance of Counsel for his defense."
- Sixth Amendment, United States Constitution

"Excessive bail shall not be required, nor excessive fines imposed, nor cruel and unusual punishments inflicted."
- Eighth Amendment, United States Constitution

Chapter 35. The Indictment

Antonio Pontón was indicted for murder in the first degree. His first arraignment was on October 31, 1914. The Grand Jury met on December 7, the Indictment document was filed on December 14, and the arraignment was recorded in the Indictment document as December 16, 1914.

His plea was not guilty by reason of insanity.

The *New York Penal Code, Article 94 § 1044 (1915)*, defined murder in first degree as "The killing of a human being, unless it is excusable or justifiable ... when committed: 1. From a deliberate and premeditated design to effect the death of the person killed, or of another ..." Under *The New York Penal Code, Article 94 § 1045 (1915)*, murder in the first degree was punishable by death.

. . .

"*County of Schenectady, Supreme Court. The People of New York Against Antonio Ponton.*" Alexander T. Blessing, District Attorney of Schenectady County, sat as he typed the charge in the Indictment document, careful to cover all the elements of the crime of murder in the first degree. The *premeditation* aspect was critical and necessary for him to secure the ultimate penalty of death.

In the document, time and time again Blessing identified the murderer, the victim, the weapon used for the killing, and emphasized the *mens rea* or guilty state of mind of the killer, his *willful intent* and *malice aforethought*, the manner in which the killing was inflicted, the place and date of the deed.

"*The said Antonio Ponton, on the second day of October nineteen hundred and fourteen at the City of Schenectady in this Schenectady County did on the day and at the place aforesaid, feloniously, willfully with malice aforethought, and with the deliberate and premeditated design to effect the death of one Bessie S. Kromer, make an assault upon her, the said Bessie S. Kromer, then and there being and the said Antonio Ponton with a knife or dirk, feloniously, willfully, with malice aforethought, and with the deliberate and premeditated design to effect the death of her, the said Bessie S. Kromer, the said Antonio Ponton did then and there, with the said knife or dirk, which said knife or dirk, he the said Antonio Ponton, then and there had and held in his hand, strike, cut, bruise and mortally wound her, the said Bessie S. Kromer, and inflict upon the body and person of her, the said Bessie S. Kromer, certain knife or dirk wounds and injuries, from which knife or dirk wounds and injuries, she, the said Bessie S. Kromer, shortly thereafter died, and that the death of her, the said Bessie S. Kromer, was caused and produced by the aforesaid knife or dirk wounds and injuries inflicted as aforesaid, and that the aforesaid knife or dirk wounds and injuries were inflicted as aforesaid by the said Antonio Ponton with force and arms, feloniously, willfully and of his malice aforethought, and with the deliberate and premeditated design to effect the death of her, the said Bessie S. Kromer, the said Antonio Ponton, in manner and form aforesaid, and by the means aforesaid, did kill and slay her, the said Bessie S. Kromer, against the form of the statute in such case made and provided."*

The document seemed never-ending. He covered everything.

The Grand Jury had all the right people in it to move the case forward. The foreman, *Clarence W. Bradshaw*, was a bank clerk and witnessed the crime. The other witnesses sworn before the Grand Jury were *Charles F. Engel*, the policeman arresting Antonio, also witness to the crime; *Arthur Magee*, a policeman; *J. J. Burke M.D.*, the doctor who performed the autopsy on Bessie Kromer's body; *Orley Eckerson*, the owner of the food store where Antonio and Bessie argued prior to the murder; *James F. Whalen*, the store clerk who witnessed Bessie and Antonio arguing; *Bernard J. Waterman*, the *Schenectady Gazette* reporter who took Antonio's statement; *Nora Kromer*, Bessie's mother; *Miss Rice*, a witness who saw Antonio strike Bessie in front of her house; *Walter Vogel*, a witness to the crime; *Emma Van Nattan*, a witness to the crime; *Louis A. Welch, Jr.*, the Schenectady Jail Sheriff; *James Turner*, an electrical works assembler and witness to the crime; and *John Holt*, an instructor at General Electric and witness to the crime.

This was an open-and-shut case for Blessing.

The court resolved to see all criminal cases on Monday Dec. 28, 1914, except for Antonio's.

The trial was scheduled for April 19, 1915.

Chapter 36. The Players

Antonio Pontón's defense team consisted of two public defenders, county attorneys Homer J. Borst and George B. Smith of the Borst & Smith law firm in Schenectady, New York. While of competent backgrounds and good connections, Borst and Smith were young attorneys at the onset of their careers, still gaining experience in the courtroom, with no record in the area of criminal defense. They had never defended a charge of murder in the first degree. Andrew J. Nellis, a former judge from Albany experienced in death penalty matters later became *of counsel* (an advisor) to the young lawyers, and played a strong role in court on behalf of Antonio.

Attorney Homer J. Borst was an unassuming man. His brown hair parted on the left, he had a long clean-shaven face with almost no cheekbones, and projected a certain overall "good guy" image. Born in Ft. Wayne, New York in 1886, younger than Antonio, Borst graduated from Harvard Law School and moved to Schenectady in 1911, where he worked at his father's law firm and was admitted as partner in 1912. This firm later dissolved on account of his father being appointed Supreme Court Justice in 1914. Borst formed a firm in partnership with George B. Smith that year. Borst was county attorney at the time of Antonio's trial. He later became bankruptcy referee for Schenectady, Saratoga and Warren counties for many years, in addition to continuing with his practice. For the last 30 years of his life, until he passed of a sudden heart attack at 70, he was a Mohawk National Bank officer and served in various community organizations.

Attorney George B. Smith was born in Camden, New York in 1885 and was also younger than his client. He graduated from Albany Law School, where he roomed with O. Byron Brewster, who would later become a renowned New York Supreme Court judge. Smith partnered with Homer J. Borst after he graduated. Later on in his career he would become a corporate counsel of the City of Schenectady and

President of the Bar Association of Schenectady County.

After attorney and former New York judge Andrew J. Nellis (b 1852) shaved his "General Custer" moustache, he somewhat resembled Antonio's appearance, except that he was older than his father Manuel. But for Nellis' receding hairline and taller stature, the former judge-turned-defense-attorney also had wavy hair, light eyes, a square-shaped face, prominent cheekbones and a square chin, like his client, minus the dimple. Nellis was a decided and somewhat assertive man. This served him well often, but some judges disliked his eagerness in the courtroom. Nevertheless, Nellis was well respected by his peers and the community. He had been a teacher since he was 15 years old, prior to graduating from Albany Law School in 1875. After graduation, Nellis partnered with Honorable Horace Smith and his son Borden E. Smith, from 1895 until 1903. He then practiced *solo* for a few years and also litigated as partner of the Countryman, Nellis & DuBois firm. Nellis was an active Freemason, as was Antonio's father Manuel, becoming a high priest of the St. Patrick's Lodge No. 4 in Johnstown, New York for two years. He also authored a large number of law treatises, including the renowned *The Law of Street Surface Railroads*.

Concurrent with Antonio's imprisonment and throughout Antonio's trial, Nellis represented his wealthy son-in-law George W. Potter in the murder of his neighbor, John Barrett. Barret was severely beaten in his barn, which was then set on fire. Nellis secured Potter's release, and he was exonerated from the crime. The attorney also represented Mr. Potter's employee, Lewis M. Roach, who after recanting a confession stating that Potter forced him to do the deed due to a feud with his neighbor, ended up being convicted for the crime and executed on the electric chair on September 3, 1915.

. . .

District Attorney Alexander T. Blessing and Assistant District Attorney George W. Featherstonhaugh represented the state.

Blessing was born in Princeton, New York in 1869, and was a self-made man. He lost both his parents when he was young. Blessing graduated from Union College in 1897 by studying at night and working during the day. He read law at the law firm of Hastings & Schoolcraft and passed the New York Bar in 1900. He became District

Attorney in 1910, remaining for three terms as such.

Blessing was a svelte man with prematurely gray hair, short and parted in the middle, and a clean-shaven face. His gaze was penetrating, and he mastered eloquence. He was a man on a mission, a true avenger ... a natural actor playing an award-winning role. And this worked wonders for him in the courtroom.

Although Blessing was a Democrat, he would not accept defeat in the political arena by displaying any mercy to the killer of a young beloved teacher, even if he were mentally ill. Murdering a woman in such a heinous way deserved the ultimate penalty, regardless of the defendant's history. Blessing's political aspirations won him the race for Mayor of Schenectady in 1925.

Assistant District Attorney George W. Featherstonhaugh, Jr. was born in 1878 in New York and graduated in 1900 from Union College. He was the grandson of George W. Featherstonhaugh, the first United States Geologist and proponent of the Albany and Schenectady railroad and surveyor of portions of Louisiana for United States purchase. He was well respected and held a position of trust in the community, as his grandfather did.

. . .

Judge Charles Clark Van Kirk was born in Greenwich, New York in 1862. He graduated from Colgate University in 1884 with a Bachelor in Arts and from 1884 to 1886, he taught in the Boys' Academy in Troy. He then began the study of law and joined the New York Bar in 1888, practicing law in various firms, including the firms of Patterson, Bulkley & Van Kirk in Albany, and Roe & Van Kirk in Port Henry. He was then elected as Justice of the Supreme Court, his term expiring in 1919. He began a long elected career on the Fourth Judicial District Supreme Court in January 1, 1906 and retired at the end of 1932. Judge Van Kirk started his Appellate Division service in January 1921 and was appointed Presiding Justice in January 1928, staying in this role until he retired.

Judge Van Kirk was a blond mid-sized man with subtle eye bags, a small nose, a well-groomed moustache, and a fixed furrowed brow. In the courtroom, he dressed in the traditional black robe and bowtie. Van Kirk was conservative and demanded control of his courtroom. In his mind, right was right and wrong was wrong. There were no "gray areas."

There were no excuses.

Chapter 37. Laying the Ground for the Insanity Defense

O
n March 15, 1915, at the request of Antonio Pontón's defense counsel Homer J. Borst, Judge Van Kirk approved that a *Puerto Rico Lunacy Commission* inquire about the history of mental illness in Antonio's family as part of his insanity defense. The judge requested that its report be ready no later than April 10, 1915.

The Puerto Rico Commission would take evidence in San Juan to show that three of the defendant's relatives were insane and had been patients in an insane asylum. The defense represented that two of Antonio's cousins were discharged as cured and a third was released at the request of relatives but was not cured.

Defense attorney Borst presented an affidavit exhibiting a letter from Dr. Francisco R. de Goenaga, then Superintendent of the insane asylum at San Juan, Puerto Rico, describing the history of Antonio's relatives who resided in the asylum. Margarita Cobián Rivera was admitted to the asylum on April 1, 1905, suffering from acute melancholia and was discharged as cured on December 31, 1906. Sixto Sánchez Ortiz was admitted January 2, 1914 suffering from manic-depressive insanity, and was discharged December 15, 1914, at the request of his family, but at time of release he was not cured. Sixto's brother, Pío Sánchez Ortiz, was admitted February 6, 1906, suffering from acute mania, and was discharged as cured on October 31, 1906. The report stated that their uncle was also demented and that many members of Antonio's family on his mother's side suffered mental derangement.

For the brothers Sixto and Pío Sánchez Ortiz, the degree of insanity would linger throughout their lifetime. They were long-term patients at the *Manicomio Insular de Puerto Rico* (Puerto Rico Mental Asylum), residing there still in 1930.

Antonio's maternal heredity was tainted with insanity. There was

159

no question about it.

But yet to be discovered was an incurable disease that invaded his brain.

Antonio's will was cursed. Not once, but twice.

Chapter 38. The Jury

Antonio Pontón's trial made front page headlines across major newspapers. On April 17, 1915, the *Schenectady Gazette* headline read, "Trial of Ponton on the Charge of Committing one of Most Startling Murders in History of County."

"The trial will be the last chapter in a story of love and tragedy," the article stated. The defense and prosecution summoned over 100 witnesses. The trial was expected to take a long time and run into the evening.

There was much speculation as to whether Manuel and Etervina would travel to New York for the trial. "Ponton's parents have not forsaken him," stated the report, but it explained they were in poor health and not likely to undergo the trip and attend trial. The reports described Manuel as "of advanced age, feeble of mind and body and barely able to comprehend the events" leading to Antonio's situation.

. . .

Antonio appeared before Justice Van Kirk at the Supreme Court on Monday, April 19, 1915. The morning of April 20, 1915 was dedicated to jury selection. Opening statements were scheduled for the afternoon.

A special panel of 100 jurors was drawn on April 10, 1915 before Justice Edward C. Whitmyer. Sheriff Louis A. Welch brought Antonio into the courtroom and helped him sit by his lawyers on the defense table, facing the judge. At the sight of the jurors, the reality of his fate began to set in and Antonio broke down and wept, wiping his eyes and forehead with his handkerchief.

"Why am I here? What is happening?" he said to his lawyer, Homer Borst.

"Mr. Pontón, you killed a woman, remember?" he responded.

"I have told you before, I don't remember!" Antonio said.

"Yes, you are here for the murder of Miss Bessie Kromer, your former girlfriend," Borst said.

"I have told ju before! I don't remember killing her! I loved her! I wanted to kill myself! I remember wanting to go see her. I knew she loved me! Her mother broke us up! I remember wanting to kill myself, but I do not remember killing her! I only remember waking up in the hospital. Thees is all my mind tells me. Why can't my mind let me remember about it?"

The lawyers tried to comfort their client.

"I see visions! I do not know what is real and what is not! I am so confused!" Antonio asserted in desperation.

"We know you do not remember, Mr. Pontón. We have discussed this before. We cannot deny that you committed the crime. Many witnesses saw you do it, including the police," said Borst. "But we know you are ill and you did not know what you were doing was wrong."

Antonio paused.

"Mr. Pontón. Be patient. We will explain to the judge and to the jury that you do not remember doing the act. We will tell them you lost your will. We will explain that your mind is not working as it should be, and that you did not know right from wrong. We will try to show that to the jury," Borst said.

"But first," Smith interrupted. "We have to select twelve men from this group of people to be the jurors for your trial. These men will decide your fate," he said.

He had to trust his lawyers. Everyone insisted that he killed Bessie, so he must have. He just did not remember doing it.

Antonio's gaze shifted to the potential jurors. As he scanned them one by one, and they scanned him, he felt so different from all of them. He was from another world. Antonio recalled the letter his mother wrote to Mrs. Kromer when he first arrived to Schoharie.

"My son is all alone in a new country, facing a different language, a different culture," Etervina wrote, asking Mrs. Kromer, from one mother to another, to take good care of her son Antonio. He thought about the irony of it all. The same woman his mother asked to protect him had hurt him so.

He gazed at the hundred potential jurors once again. There were no Hispanics in the jury pool. These were the men who would decide his fate. Men who would likely not understand his culture and could misinterpret his conduct, his representations, and his intentions. Would they care enough to understand his condition?

Indeed, he was alone.

"We will ask them questions, and based on their answers we will try to select the jurors who we think will favor your case, Mr. Pontón. It is important that you let us do our job and only speak when spoken to. Do you understand?" Borst explained. "The jurors must not hear anything you say," he asserted. "We will not put you on the stand, but anything you say out loud they can hear. You need to calm down and let the process stay its course. Do you understand?" he directed.

Antonio nodded.

"This is all we are doing today," the lawyer assured Antonio.

After his attorneys explained the protocol of the preliminary proceedings and gave him direction, Antonio calmed down some, but he was overwhelmed. He stayed put through jury selection, as his lawyers directed.

Twelve men were selected through the *voir dire* process, where both the defense and the prosecution lawyers questioned each candidate to choose the best suitors to their case.

The press published the names of the jurors that would hear the evidence and decide the guilt or innocence of Antonio:

1. Charles M. Cox, mechanic, 43 Parkwood Boulevard.
2. Charles L. Wick, bookkeeper for James F. Burns, 3 Mynderse Street.
3. Ernest W. Mincher, salesman, Alderman Tenth ward, 10 Euclid Avenue.
4. James Babbitt, machinist, G. E. Company, 232 Eighth Avenue.
5. Ernest Q. Gladdon, draughtsman, G. E. Company, 34 Elder Street.
6. Fred Neuhaus, machinist. G. E. Company, 824 Lincoln Avenue.
7. Sanford Hedden, farmer, Glenville.
8. Charles G. Schmidt, manager, coal company, 127 Glenwood Boulevard.
9. Frank Hein, molder, G. E. Company, Stop 5, Albany road.
10. Tunis Hotaling, carpenter, South Schenectady.
11. Garrett V. Baker, machinist, G. E. Company, 1727 Eastern

Avenue.

12. George S. Clare, realty dealer, 1028 Eastern Avenue.

. . .

Antonio, being Puerto Rican, was not yet a citizen of the United States. Although Puerto Rico had become a territory of the United States after the Spanish-American War of 1898, Puerto Ricans would not become citizens until 1917 under the *Jones-Safroth Act*. Nevertheless, he was entitled to all the constitutional protections afforded to any criminal defendant, whether citizen or not, including *the right to an impartial jury, drawn from a cross-section of the community*.

The New York Constitution had codified the right to an impartial jury afforded under the 6th amendment, among many of the other rights enumerated in the United States Constitution. Although the United States constitutional rights were not acknowledged as "passed down" to all the states through the 14th Amendment's Due Process Clause until well after Antonio's trial, states that adopted trial by jury were subject to the jury *impartiality* requirement.

The *cross-section requirement* has been debated with frequency over the years, both race and gender playing a specific role in court rulings reversing judgments violating this right. Even as early as 1879, the United States Supreme Court in *Strauder v. West Virginia*, 100 U.S. 303, ruled that it violates the Equal Protection Clause to exclude African Americans [non-whites] from juries. There were no Puerto Rican or Hispanic jurors in Antonio's jury pool. The total population of Schenectady in 1910 was about 72,000 and by 1915 it was about 90,000. By 1920 about 12,000 Puerto Ricans had moved to New York, many of them settling in Schenectady as laborers.

Even though he was white, Antonio was considered "non-white," or "of a different race," because he was a "Porto Rican" or "a Spaniard." The law did not afford a non-white defendant the right to have a jury of his race. However, a defendant's constitutional right to an impartial jury dictated that the jury be *drawn from a cross-section of the community* and that *race could not be used to disqualify jurors from serving*. This right was violated in Antonio's trial. Competent defense counsel would have never passed up an opportunity to include a Puerto Rican or Hispanic juror in the jury, if given the chance.

Today, it is widely accepted that race places a key role in juror's decisions, with particularity in murder cases where the victim is white and the defendant is considered of a different race, as in Antonio's situation. Having a Hispanic or Puerto Rican person in the jury would have served to help balance any racial bias against Antonio.

. . .

All jurors in Antonio's trial were male because women were not allowed to serve as jurors in the United States until well into the 20th century, despite the "cross-section requirement." The United States Supreme Court in *Strauder v. West Virginia* continued to sanction this practice, stating that even though jury service could no longer be restricted to whites under the 14th Amendment, it could continue to be restricted to males.

Many states continued the practice of all-male juries, even after the 19th Amendment extended the right to vote to women in 1920. The rationale behind the denial was based on protectionist and discriminatory arguments against women. These alleged, among other reasons, that women could not comprehend the complicated nature of the trials, they would abandon their homes, and they would be offended by the trials themselves.

The 1957 Civil Rights Act required that women be included on federal jury lists, but the Act did not affect state practices. By 1973, all 50 states permitted women jurors, but 19 provided women with exemptions not available to men, resulting in the underrepresentation of women in juries. In 1975, the United States Supreme Court in *Taylor v. Louisiana*, 419 U.S. 552, held that the practice of excluding women from juries who did not indicate their willingness to serve was unconstitutional because it deprived the accused of a jury drawn from a cross-section of the community.

. . .

An additional factor weighing in on Antonio's jury selection (although profession and social class do not rise to the same status as race or gender in the "impartial jury and cross-section debate") was that almost half of the jurors were employees of General Electric, as was a large part of the Schenectady labor force during that time. By

1918, about 70 percent of the skilled labor and 22 percent of the population of Schenectady (about 20,000 employees) worked for General Electric. Most of these workers were from a middle-low class and were blue-collar laborers. Such a slanted jury was bound to insert prejudice against Antonio.

In 1915, Antonio Pontón, a Puerto Rican defendant who murdered a white woman, was at the mercy of an all-white male jury with not much education. This was a *non-impartial* jury *not drawn* from a cross-section of the community, contrary to the right afforded to Antonio by the New York Constitution, which had adopted the due process rights afforded a criminal defendant under the United States Constitution.

All odds were against Antonio.

Chapter 39. Disgraceful Scenes at the Courthouse

O n April 22, 1915 the *Schenectady Gazette* reported "the largest crowd and the most disgraceful scenes ever witnessed in the Schenectady County Courthouse."

Antonio Pontón's murder trial drew the attention of top newspapers at local, state and national levels in the United States, as well as in Puerto Rico. The tragedy had now turned into a spectacle. An unruly crowd amassed at the Schenectady Court's doorsteps, starved for the performance yet to come. Those unable to secure admittance created an enormous disturbance.

The Schenectady Courthouse had just been relocated in 1913 from a 1831 two-story 51,000 square foot Greek Revival building on 108 Union Street, to a much larger new five-story building on 612 State Street, around the corner from the Schenectady County Jail on Veneer Street.

The new Courthouse's white façade had eight enormous pillars, two of them offset to the front, framing the central steps leading to the three main entrance arched doors. A stone-carved armored female bust, representing the fight for justice, adorned the top of each entrance door. A small gargoyle decorated the head of each bust, so as to repel evil away from the new palace of justice. Past the entry doors, to the left of the building, past the stairwell, stood the courtroom where Antonio would be tried.

The courtroom was a large hall of over 4,000 square feet in size. The gaze of a visitor entering the courtroom would immediately travel towards the end of the room, to the judge's central mahogany bench elevated from the floor. On the wall behind the judge's bench read the words "Equal Justice Under Law" which stood out in golden brass against a cherry wooden background.

Antonio sat at the defendant's table, located to his left as he entered the courtroom, after walking down the central corridor, past the spectator seating area. He sat facing the judge, accompanied by his attorneys. To the right of the defendant's table, across the aisle that divided the spectator area, sat the prosecution, facing the judge, just as the defense. The jury would sit to the right of the prosecution's table, in two rows of seats located parallel to the right wall of the courtroom. From their seats, they could observe the judge, the defense, the prosecution and the spectators.

The spectators occupied every inch of seating space in the courtroom, women comprising at least half of the crowd. In addition to those admitted in the courtroom, there were about 300 spectators packing the corridor and the stairway, all wanting to take a peek at Antonio through the glass panels by the main doors. It took five men to shut the courtroom doors against the angry crowd that remained outside of the building due to space limitations. As a clerk reopened the main courtroom door to let an officer in, a few well-dressed women sneaked in with force, knocking others down as they rushed in. Undersheriff R. R. Hunt went out of the courtroom to quiet the disturbance.

Mrs. Kromer attended the trial accompanied by her son Charles and a friend. Clerks escorted them in, and they sat in the first row of the spectators' area behind the prosecution's table.

Mrs. Kromer and Antonio sat within a few feet of each other. She stared at him with angry eyes, while commenting on his appearance.

Chapter 40. The Prosecution's Case

"**S**he was the most beautiful baby girl who grew to become the perfect daughter and a beloved teacher," said George W. Featherstonbaugh Jr., Assistant District Attorney, who opened for the prosecution.

Featherstonbaugh gave an emotional account of Bessie's childhood since birth and described her life before Antonio Pontón arrived in Schoharie.

Judge Van Kirk leaned forward on his bench. The jurors were attentive to Featherstonbaugh's story.

"This is one of the most brutal killings in the criminal history of the county," Featherstonbaugh warned the jury. To the defense's surprise, given the evidence to the contrary, Featherstonbaugh asserted, "Miss Kromer did not correspond to her killer's love in any way and just wanted a friendship."

He told the jury Antonio promised Mrs. Kromer that he would stop pursuing her daughter, although Mrs. Kromer and Antonio never crossed words regarding the matter.

Featherstonbaugh then provided a factual account of the events culminating with Bessie's death. He assured the jury that "the evil killer sitting in this room today was not satisfied with murdering Miss Kromer, but he also wanted to assassinate her character! He took advantage of the opportunity to do so in the statement he gave the newspaper reporter, Mr. Bernie Waterman, at Ellis Hospital. He murdered her, not once, but twice!"

"The People intend to prove premeditated murder in the first degree because the murder of Miss Kromer was a carefully planned act with a well-defined motive," the Assistant District Attorney closed.

To overcome the defense, the prosecution had to prove that Antonio Pontón was sane at the time he committed the crime, *beyond a reasonable doubt*. This was their burden of proof.

. . .

About 100 witnesses waited to provide their accounts of the murder, if called by the prosecution. The People called its eyewitnesses to recount the gruesome details of the murder, not to prove that Antonio was the murderer, as the defense had already admitted to Antonio committing the act. The prosecutors' strategy was to immerse the jurors' minds in the brutal aspects of the crime and secure the death penalty.

Mrs. Kromer cried for part of the opening statement and witness accounts, while Antonio sat with his hands on his face, holding a handkerchief, looking down, and sobbing out loud at times during witness testimony.

The jurors could not keep their eyes off Mrs. Kromer.

District Attorney Blessing called the first witness, Dr. Joseph J. Burke, who performed the autopsy on Bessie's body.

Burke testified, "There were a number of fatal wounds that would have caused her death in less than a minute, due to hemorrhage. There was one wound that severed the carotid artery, one that penetrated the heart, and various ones that penetrated the heart and the lung. In total, there were fifteen wounds, major and minor."

Coroner E. H. Jackson was called next.

The coroner corroborated Dr. Burke's testimony as to the wounds and recounted his activity the day of the murder, visiting the scene and later the hospital where Antonio was being treated for three self-inflicted knife wounds on his chest area. He spoke about the evidence he gathered from Bessie's and Antonio's bodies and their living quarters, including letters and photographs. He identified a knife Chief of Police Rynex gave him as being a Bowie knife about seven inches long, stained with blood.

On cross-examination by defense attorney Nellis, Jackson said that one of Antonio's wounds was about one inch from his heart.

Nellis also secured the letters Bessie and Antonio wrote to each other, after objection from prosecutors. It was evident that the prosecution had withheld the letters from the defense attorneys so that they would be unable to review them prior to trial. Yet, the court did not reprimand the District Attorney's office for this practice.

After Jackson was dismissed, Police Sergeant C. F. A. Engel of the third precinct provided a recount of the night of the murder consistent with what he had relayed to the press that night. He said that he was walking around the area with his dog, about 200 feet from the scene, when he heard Bessie scream. He testified that when he turned, he saw Antonio strike Bessie twice on the chest; that when Bessie tried to get away towards the street, Antonio followed her and stabbed her again on her back; then Engel said he saw Bessie fall to the ground. He testified that when Antonio saw him coming towards him and Bessie, Antonio began to run away in the direction of Backus St. and Engel followed him with his dog, catching up to Antonio, the dog biting him. Sergeant Engel stated that he overtook Antonio after he stabbed himself and fell to the ground. Engel then took away Antonio's knife and gave it to mounted patrolman Kennedy, who had just arrived. Engel identified the knife in court and spoke about sending Antonio to the hospital. On cross-examination, Sergeant Engel answered that there was enough light in the area, and that he recognized the man stabbing Bessie Kromer as Antonio Pontón.

Patrolman J. H. Kennedy then corroborated Engel's testimony and the turnover of the knife to Chief Rynex. He also stated, "I saw the defendant in the area many times before, around the Conde House where Miss Kromer roomed, including earlier the day of the events."

J. Francis Whelan was 17 years old and worked as a clerk of the O. J. Eckerson grocery store located opposite to the scene of the crime. He testified supporting the earlier testimony by the officers regarding the manner of the stabbing.

Likewise, Walter Vogel, 19 years old, was a witness to the events and verified the previous witnesses' testimony.

Miss Irene Rice appeared to be the witness closest to the scene and offered more detail as to the acts. She said, "Mr. Pontón and Miss Kromer were standing in front of my residence. He was facing her. I saw him strike her on her chest. When she turned to run away from him, he struck her in the back again." Miss Rice corroborated Engel's story. She said she knew Bessie in person and Antonio by sight from previous occasions he had been in the area with Bessie.

James Turner and Emma Van Nattan testified validating the other witnesses' stories.

John Carey, a streetcar conductor, testified about Antonio Pontón boarding his car the day of the murder and also on other occasions. He said, "Mr. Pontón boarded my car about twice a week around midnight, prior to the events of the crime. I saw him board around suppertime with a woman recently, but I don't remember the exact date." He then provided details as to what streets Antonio boarded on, showing that he boarded close to Bessie's apartment.

District Attorney Blessing then called Bernie J. Waterman, the reporter for the *Schenectady Gazette*, and asked him to read out loud the statement Antonio gave him at Ellis Hospital within an hour or so after he was admitted with self-inflicted knife wounds.

"Objection!" defense attorney Nellis said, opposing the introduction of the statement Antonio gave Waterman. "The statement is a constitutional violation, Your Honor!"

"Not so quick, Mr. Nellis," said Van Kirk. "Lay the ground for your objection."

The court allowed Nellis to question Waterman.

"Mr. Waterman, did you or anyone tell Mr. Pontón, while he was laying on his hospital bed, mortally wounded and semi-sedated that anything he said could be used against him in a court of law?" said Nellis.

"No," the reporter responded.

"Was there anyone else in the room with you and Mr. Pontón at the time you say you took his statement?" asked Nellis.

"No," the reporter responded. "I was the only one in the room with Mr. Pontón."

"Your Honor, I object to the admission of the statement taken by Mr. Waterman from Mr. Pontón on grounds that the statement violates Mr. Pontón's constitutional rights under the Fifth and Sixth Amendments," said Nellis to the court.

In the United States Bill of Rights, the Fifth Amendment (which grants the right against self-incrimination, among others) and Fourteenth Amendment due process and equal protection guarantees extend to all "persons." The Sixth amendment rights attaching to criminal trials, including the right to a public trial, a trial by an impartial jury, the assistance of counsel, and the right to confront adverse witnesses, all apply to "the accused." The New York Constitution at the time of Antonio's trial incorporated the cited United States Bill of Rights, which applied to Antonio as a person and an accused, even if he were not yet a citizen of the United States.

"Objection overruled," said Van Kirk with no explanation.

Antonio's statement to Waterman made it into the record.

Nellis took exceptions to be presented on appeal. The court

allowed the exceptions, and Waterman was dismissed.

Next, Chief Rynex testified about having received the knife from a patrolman and turning it over to the coroner.

At 4:15 p.m. Attorney Nellis requested a recess, which Judge Van Kirk granted. Nellis was worried, as the Lunacy Commission depositions from Puerto Rico had not yet arrived.

As Antonio was transported back to jail by foot, countless people blocked the sidewalk by the old fire station to get a glimpse of him.

He had become a circus attraction, like Topsy the elephant.

. . .

Witnesses for the Prosecution completed their testimony the morning of April 21, 1915. The testimony of Jeremiah J. Cullen and Mrs. Kromer were most salient.

Jeremiah Cullen, a clerk in the Albany Hardware and Iron Company, identified Antonio as being the man who on September of 1914 bought the knife used to commit the crime.

As Mrs. Nora Kromer took the stand during the morning, Antonio created a scene for all to see. He rose from his seat, a wild creature, waving his arms and shouting to Mrs. Kromer in Spanish. The press described him as "a maniac."

And he was.

"¡Vieja bruja! ¡Maldita! (Old witch! Damn you!)" he screamed. "If ju had not interfered! I would still be in loskool! Besi and I would be together!" he blamed Mrs. Kromer for the ultimate fate of her daughter and his own. "You liar! You had me arrested with lies! I never had a revolver! You liar! Ju made her write the letters. She told me!"

"Your Honor, may we have a short recess, please," asked defense attorney Borst.

The court gave the defense a ten-minute recess.

The jury witnessed the entire display of anger by Antonio, who calmed down, aided by his attorneys.

Back from recess, as Mrs. Kromer proceeded to testify, Antonio's eyes pierced her with hatred. He looked as if he was ready to spring at her.

The jurors watched. Everyone did.

Mrs. Kromer testified about when Antonio first stayed as a

boarder in her house on 27 Main Street in Schoharie.

"He arrived sometime in June of 1911," she said, mistakenly.

She also testified about the trip Bessie and she took to Columbia University the summer of 1914. "He stalked her all the time, and she did not want to have anything to do with him," she said. "There, I saw them have an altercation, and my daughter told him 'I have told you repeatedly that I will not leave my mother for anyone,'" she said. "He had the nerve to ask her to leave me!" she said.

Mrs. Kromer declared under oath that she did not know about Bessie's romantic relationship with Antonio. She said that they were just friends and her daughter did not want anything to do with Antonio, romantically.

The press reported that Mrs. Kromer testified as a "self-possessed" woman, often "sarcastic and with a grin."

"The nerve of the man, blaming me for her death," she whispered at her son Charles after she left the witness stand. "I did what any other mother would have done to protect her child!"

To her, it was only fair to put to death the monster that murdered her beloved daughter. A life for a life. Justice shall be served.

The prosecution rested at 11:52 a.m.

Chapter 41. The Defense's Case

Attorney Homer J. Borst opened for the defense just before the afternoon recess on April 21, 1915.

"The fact that Mr. Pontón committed the crime is not denied," he said. "But Mr. Pontón was insane at the time of the act. His insanity was inherited from his mother's family. The defense will also show that he was, and still is, ill with a dementia-causing disease that has invaded his brain."

The jurors listened.

"The father of Antonio Pontón was a high-born Spaniard," Borst continued. "He went to Porto Rico and married a native woman several years ago. In the early days of Porto Rico there were many cases of intermarriages, which caused much disease and insanity, especially in this class. Pontón's mother had tainted blood and a vein of insanity, which her son inherited. Insanity ran in Mrs. Pontón's family," Borst assured.

"The defense will prove, by a preponderance of the evidence, that when Mr. Pontón committed the crime, he did not realize what he was doing was wrong because he was insane," he said.

The defense had to prove Antonio's insanity by a *preponderance of the evidence*. This proof was key to obtaining an excuse from the death penalty under New York's strict law. This standard of proof was lower than the *beyond reasonable doubt* standard that the prosecution had to meet to secure the death penalty for Antonio.

"Mr. Pontón and Miss Kromer were lovers," Borst continued. "After years together, she turned him down, at the request of her mother, even though she loved him," he said. "Mr. Pontón became depressed and wanted to kill himself."

"Mr. Pontón bought the knife for the purpose of committing suicide, not for the purpose of killing Miss Kromer," said the defense lawyer.

"On the day of the crime," Borst told the jurors, "he went to see her one last time before he killed himself. He was desperate, overcome by insanity. And he lost his will."

Judge Van Kirk rested back on his bench chair.

Reverend Charles M. Karg, Pastor of the Schoharie Lutheran Church and Kromer family friend, was the first witness called by defense attorney George B. Smith.

"I knew of Miss Bessie Kromer's and Mr. Pontón's affair. Everyone knew. It was difficult not to notice," he testified. "The summer before the incident, Mrs. Kromer requested that I help Mr. Pontón with his personal situation," he said. "I had helped him with his English before, when he first arrived in July of 1911 and during the year he lived at the Kromer's," he said.

Borst asked the witness, "Reverend Karg, in your opinion, was Mrs. Kromer aware of Mr. Pontón's and Miss Kromer's romantic relationship?"

"Yes she was," he responded. "When she asked that I help Mr. Pontón the summer of 1914, she suggested that he was likely going to stay with the family for an indefinite period of time," he said. "She had to have known. Everyone in town knew. It was obvious they were a serious couple," he said.

"And what is your opinion of the young man, Mr. Pontón, Reverend?" asked Borst.

"He seemed like a good man. Really cared about her. Diligent in his studies. But he did have problems with his health. He suffered many headaches and also lacked focus. This affected his studies. The language barrier did not help, but he was resolved to overcome it. And he eventually did. His English greatly improved, and he was fluent by the time he left for law school. He did seem depressed at times, particularly the summer of 1914. He seemed very sick then," he said.

"Thank you Pastor Karg, no more questions for now," said Borst, dismissing the witness.

. . .

The afternoon session began with the defense calling Miguel de la Rosa, a Puerto Rican friend of the Pontón family and a medical student at the University of Maryland. De la Rosa testified regarding the Pontón family and the history of insanity on Antonio's mother's side. He explained that in Antonio's hometown of Comerío, "with a population of about eight to ten thousand, everyone was related to everyone else, through intermarriage." He also said that some of Antonio's relatives had been admitted to insane asylums. He described Antonio had always been nervous, and often complained of headaches that were more frequent at night, but occurred throughout the day, as well.

Antonio López, an Albany Law School student from Puerto Rico, corroborated de la Rosa's testimony as far as Antonio being nervous, forgetful and "addicted to headaches." He said "Mr. Pontón often searched for his hat or other property when he had them on his person."

Stanley Bliss, also an Albany Law School student, corroborated the testimony by de la Rosa and López. Antonio was always nervous, was forgetful and had headaches.

Charles Watson, the Albany Law School Registrar, testified that Antonio was a poor student and had to repeat some of his second-year courses. He shared some of his grades and identified his handwriting on letters.

Coroner, Dr. E. H. Jackson testified about retrieving about 50 letters from Antonio's room, all containing the same woman's handwriting, and giving them to the district attorney. Defense attorney Nellis secured the letters for examination over the prosecution's objections.

Dr. Jackson testified again as to his examination of Bessie Kromer's body and his inferences from his examination. In addition, he testified that he retrieved three identical photographs from Bessie's room showing Bessie and Antonio standing on the back of a car platform labeled "Coney Island." He gave two to the press and kept one.

Dr. Jackson also spoke about Antonio's condition at the Ellis Hospital and described Antonio's reaction when the doctor informed him about his crime. He said, "Mr. Pontón was nervous, incoherent, and his facial veins stood out." The coroner also spoke about retrieving documents from Bessie's room, including letters. In total, there were 82 letters recovered.

The next witness, Mrs. Chamberlain, was Antonio's former landlady. She described an episode when she found Antonio in his room with all windows shut and a strong smell of gas, and added that she called her nephew over, who found a letter by Antonio addressed to his law school class, that seemed to be a suicide note. Douglas Wiger, Mrs. Chamberlain's nephew, also testified and corroborated her testimony.

Eugene Vera, a Puerto Rican student at Albany Law School, confirmed that Antonio was nervous, had poor memory and had headaches.

So did Mrs. Rose Van Guysling, of 253 North Pearl Street in Albany, where Antonio had boarded. She testified, "Mr. Pontón was peculiar. He was often nervous and had a poor memory. He also complained of continued headache." She added that she had seen Antonio carrying many letters from a woman named Bessie, and that he had told her that he was going to marry Bessie.

Mrs. Charlotte Gebhardt, an English teacher from Schoharie, testified contradicting the former testimony by Mrs. Kromer, where she said that she did not approve of Antonio and had no knowledge of his relationship with Bessie. Mrs. Gebhardt stated, "Mrs. Kromer asked me to tutor the young man in English while he stayed in Schoharie. She told me he was staying with them to live at their home for a while and suggested that he was in a serious relationship with Bessie Kromer." Mrs. Gebhardt also testified that Antonio had complained of headaches while being tutored by her, and she had given him medication for his headaches.

Mrs. Gebhardt was the last defense witness.

Testimony closed at 4:50 p.m. on April 21, 1915.

Chapter 42. The Experts

On April 22, 1915 medical expert witnesses testified as to Antonio's physical and mental condition. Guy Fish, a medical student at the Albany Medical College, was the first witness that day. He testified that he took a blood sample from Antonio the previous week. Dr. Ellis Kellert, Director of the Bender Laboratory in Albany and Professor of Pathology and Bacteriology at the Albany Medical College, was then called by the defense, and he testified that the blood test performed confirmed the presence of syphilis in Antonio's blood.

Defense attorney Borst called Dr. Charles L. Bailey, an *alienist* (a specialist in treating mental diseases), as the insanity medical expert for the defense. The doctor was short and stocky, had tiny eyes and bushy brown-gray eyebrows. Dr. Bailey was born in Troy, New York in 1870, graduated from Flower Hospital Medical School in New York in 1891, and established his psychiatry practice in Albany, qualifying as an expert in lunacy in 1900. He was a reputable physician with close to 25 years of experience by the time of Antonio's trial. Bailey had also worked as a Coroner's physician. In 1917, he became Albany's Lieutenant Surgeon during World War I. He spoke with frequency about various health topics, and also authored a book, *Legal Medicine*, which he published in 1927. By then he had testified more than 3,000 times in more than 500 court cases, including 57 murder trials, in matters dealing with mental disorders and questions of sanity.

After Dr. Bailey testified as to his qualifications as an insanity expert, he proceeded to speak about his medical examination of Antonio on Friday, April 17, 1915.

"My examination of Antonio Pontón showed an abnormal or subnormal mental state," said the doctor. "Mr. Pontón acquired an infectious disease of the blood and cerebral insanity due to syphilis, together with an inherited mental derangement. He is unable to add simple sums and has trouble pronouncing words beyond a normal language barrier. When I pointed a finger at Mr. Pontón and said to him: 'You killed Bessie Kromer,' he replied 'Bessie Kromer? Taken from me?' as he pointed at his own wounds saying, 'Kill myself, love Bessie Kromer.'"

Dr. Bailey also testified about asking Antonio some questions regarding his religious faith, and he shared that Antonio did not know the differences between the Catholic and Protestant religions, and he had also stated that (the Apostles) Matthew, Mark and Luke were "good men."

"What else did you find as a result of your examination, Dr. Bailey," continued the defense.

"Mr. Pontón is in the third stage of syphilis," the doctor revealed. "The disease has spread to his brain."

Repeated sounds of "Awh!" filled the courtroom.

The judge leaned forward on his bench.

"Order in the court!" he said, while banging his gavel on a wooden soundblock on his bench.

Borst asked the doctor to explain the nature of the disease.

"Syphilis is a venereal infection that, if left untreated, could spread to the brain and infect the central nervous system. When it invades the brain, the condition is called *neurosyphilis*. Patients with neurosyphilis, such as Mr. Pontón, typically suffer apathy, seizures and dementia, and often aneurisms, if the disease affects the cardiovascular system," he said.

"How can this disease be contracted, Dr. Bailey?" asked Nellis.

"There are two ways the disease can be contracted. The first is through sexual intercourse, and the second is at birth. When the disease is contracted at birth, it is referred to as *congenital syphilis*," the doctor said.

"What impact does the disease of syphilis have on those who carry the congenital form of the disease, doctor?" asked Nellis.

"Well, if *congenital* or contracted at birth, this condition results in deformities and blindness. And for all those who carry the disease, congenital or not, if left untreated, more than half of those infected die from it," he said.

"Dr. Bailey, what impact has the disease had on Mr. Pontón?" asked Nellis.

"Mr. Pontón had not been treated for the disease, and therefore it is quite advanced. It has spread to his brain, causing him the symptoms I described earlier, in particular, dementia," the doctor said. "His *neurosyphilis* has made him insane. As a result of the illness, Mr. Pontón is a creature of impulse and cannot make the premeditated plans alleged by the prosecution."

He further explained that being in prison would accelerate the progress of the disease, due to the stressful environment of confinement.

Antonio's attorneys did not introduce in the record any evidence regarding the incidence of syphilis in society, and they missed the opportunity to educate the jurors in hopes of mitigating any bias the men could develop towards Antonio for having "a loathsome disease."

The reality was that around the turn of the century, syphilis was a public health disaster in the United States and in many parts of the world. In 1915, at least 20 percent of the population was estimated to have syphilis. Due to its social stigma and the lack of knowledge about the disease, it went undisclosed, so the actual percentages are estimated to be much greater, in particular for men in the military. United States Army soldiers in Puerto Rico were reported to have almost a 40 percent incidence in 1915 and 13 percent of these soldiers suffered from syphilis dementia.

The public was uneducated about the disease and its prevalence. Any discussion of syphilis resided in specialized books and in medical journals not accessible by the general public. Also, somewhat hypocritically, society viewed syphilis as a subject beyond the "boundaries of decency," thought to be a disorder that affected only the immoral. Yet, it knew no social class boundaries.

This social taboo did nothing to help reduce the spread of the disease, for which there was no effective cure at the time, as the penicillin treatment for syphilis would not arrive until much later, in 1943. Existing treatment, *mercury* and *Salvarsan*, did not cure the disease and could only alleviate some of the symptoms. Some treatments even caused severe physiological side effects.

Physicians tried to help enlighten the public by representing that syphilis did not punish fairly, and that some of the most promiscuous people were spared, while some of the more innocent were not. Although the increase in the disease prompted the beginning of public education and regulatory standards, this still did not reduce the stigma associated with carrying syphilis.

To worsen matters, the *Eugenics* movement, which promoted the elimination of the sick, the insane, those with "poor genetics," and those belonging to a "lesser race," fueled the "loathsome disease" stigma. The prevailing cultural and social environment would cast a shadow that obscured any potential ray of sympathy the jurors could develop towards Antonio and his condition. From this perspective, the odds for Antonio's defense to prevail in trial were low, if not inexistent.

The defense rested their expert witness examination at 11:26 a.m. on April 22, 1915.

. . .

That afternoon, the prosecution called two witnesses to rebut the defense's expert testimony, Drs. Jessee M. W. Scott and Nishan A. Pashayan.

Dr. Jessee Melville White Scott was born in 1872 in New York and graduated from Albany Medical College in 1896. At commencement he was honored for being best student in his class, where he received the highest grade in the *obstetrics and surgical instruments* final examination. Thereafter, he secured a position at the Matteawan State Hospital and then went on to work at Ellis Hospital in neuro-psychiatry. He often worked with Dr. Pashayan in various levels and capacities, including making public speaking engagements together.

Dr. Scott, a 5' 11" tall brunette with green-gray eyes and a long face, detailed his experience with insane patients and his study on the defendant. He testified regarding several examinations he and Dr. Pashayan conducted on Antonio. He said they conducted three examinations in total, two on December 3, 1914 and one on April 9, 1915.

"Mr. Pontón was normal on tests of reflex," Dr. Scott testified. "He said to us 'I love Bessie Kromer, and I am going to marry her.' He became excited when we mentioned the crime or his relationship with Miss Kromer. He knew he was in jail but did not know how he had arrived there. When asked whether he knew if Miss Kromer was alive or not, Mr. Pontón relayed that he did not know whether she was alive or not, but that she would come to him if she were alive."

"Dr. Scott, was Mr. Pontón insane the night he murdered Ms. Kromer, doctor?" asked Blessing.

"Antonio Pontón was not insane on October 2, 1914," the doctor concluded.

Under cross-examination, defense attorney Nellis asked Dr. Scott about the time, place and conditions of the medical examinations.

"Dr. Scott," said Nellis. "Did you take any blood tests of Mr. Pontón?"

"No," replied Dr. Scott.

"Why not?" asked Nellis.

"We did not think it was necessary," responded Scott. "But those taken by the defense did not reveal the stage of the disease," he said, rushing to defend why perhaps he should have taken a sample.

The doctor also stated that Antonio did not recall giving an interview or statement to the *Schenectady Gazette* reporter. He further testified that he and Dr. Pashayan did not take any notes whatsoever during their examinations and that he was testifying from memory.

"Your Honor, may the defense approach the jury with Mr. Pontón, so that he can show the jury his skin lesions, reflective of his disease?" Nellis asked the judge, while Dr. Scott remained on the stand.

"Yes, you may," said Judge Van Kirk.

The defense approached as requested, and also showed the lesions to Dr. Scott, the judge and Dr. Pashayan, the next witness.

"The current lesions might have surfaced since our examination last December," he said, implying that he did not see any lesions during said examination.

Nellis then asked Dr. Scott whether he knew of any other blood test that could have been performed on Antonio that would be more suited to diagnose and assess his disease than the one performed by the defense. Dr. Scott stated that he was unsure of whether there would have been a better blood test than the one performed on Antonio to determine with specificity the degree of advancement of disease.

"The test performed by the defense was the correct test for the identification of a presence of syphilis in the bloodstream," the doctor confirmed.

"Thank you Dr. Scott. Nothing more for now," Nellis dismissed the witness.

The prosecution then called its next expert witness, Dr. Pashayan.

Dr. Nishan A. Pashayan was Schenectady's first practicing psychiatrist when psychiatry was an emerging field. He was born in

1872 in Armenia and migrated to America in 1894 to avoid the persecution of the Armenians by the Ottomans. Dr. Pashayan had a professional appearance. He was about 5' 7" tall and had dark complexion. His black hair had begun to gray on the sides. He had a dimple on his chin, a prominent nose and a thick black medium-sized moustache. The doctor attended Albany Medical College in 1895, where he studied internal medicine, general pathology and neurology. He graduated in 1901 and became involved with psychiatry (then known as "mental hygiene") and worked in various mental asylums. Pashayan left his work with the New York State psychiatric hospital network in 1907 and opened his first psychiatric office in Schenectady after he married Charlotte Hume. While at Schenectady, he was Vice-Chairman of the Ellis Hospital Medical Board and President of the Schenectady County Medical Society. He often worked and lectured with Dr. Scott.

Dr. Pashayan corroborated part of Dr. Scott's testimony and added new testimony. He stated that during the doctors' medical examination, Antonio Pontón told him that his anxiety impacted his studies. The doctor said that Antonio refused to discuss his relationship with Bessie Kromer. He knew he was in New York State, but he could not remember the governor's name. He did name Wilson as the President of the United States. Dr. Pashayan said that Antonio did not remember stabbing himself or going to the hospital. He did not remember stabbing Bessie Kromer, and did not remember his interview with the *Schenectady Gazette* reporter. Dr. Pashayan also testified that he asked Antonio if he would swear he did not kill Bessie Kromer and that he would not swear this.

Dr. Pashayan also told the court that he asked Antonio if he believed that he was in his right mind at the time of his examination and he replied: "I'm all right. Why, I'm all right." Pashayan asked him whether he was in the right mind at the time of the crime. The doctor told the court that Antonio responded, "I don't know. I don't remember about it."

According to Dr. Pashayan, he performed the most comprehensive test on December 24, 1914 and testified that the results did not reveal insanity. This date was inconsistent with the dates provided by Dr. Scott in his previous testimony. Dr. Pashayan said that he asked Antonio again if he had killed Bessie Kromer and Antonio replied: "I swear I don't know. Why should I kill her?"

On cross-examination, defense attorney Nellis asked Dr. Pashayan, "Doctor, did you relay to Mr. Pontón prior to your examination at the jail that you and Dr. Scott were there to examine him at the order of the district attorney and that he was entitled to legal counsel to be present during the medical examination?

Dr. Pashayan replied, "I did not tell Mr. Pontón these things."

Attorney Nellis then asked Dr. Pashayan, "Did you inform Mr. Pontón that anything he said, even submitting his body for examination, and any information obtained from the examination or provided by him to you or Dr. Scott could be used against him in a court of law?"

"No, we did not warn Mr. Pontón of these things, except that we told him that the examination was from the District Attorney," responded Dr. Pashayan.

"Your Honor, the defense moves to strike from the record the testimony of doctors Scott and Pashayan," Nellis stated. "Their medical examinations and their testimony regarding the same violate Mr. Pontón constitutional rights. Mr. Pontón was compelled to give evidence against himself, while in custody and under duress, in violation of his constitutional rights."

"Overruled!" Judge Van Kirk denied Nellis' motion.

Nellis took an exception to the court's denial to be brought up on appeal.

Nellis then proceeded with his cross-examination of Dr. Pashayan.

"Doctor, did you or Doctor Scott take any notes of your examination of Mr. Pontón?"

"No, we did not," responded Dr. Pashayan.

"Do you know if anyone else took notes of said examinations?" asked Nellis.

"I do not know that any notes were taken," said Pashayan.

"Then, what is the basis for your testimony, if you did not keep any notes?" asked Nellis.

"Memory," the doctor replied.

"Your testimony and Dr. Scott's regarding your medical examination of Mr. Pontón, including what Mr. Pontón said to you during your examinations, is solely from memory?" asked Nellis, with a hint of sarcasm.

"Yes," Dr. Pashayan responded.

"Dr. Pashayan," said Nellis. "Can you recall every detail from an

185

examination that occurred four months and a half ago?"

"Yes, I can," responded Dr. Pashayan.

"How many patients, on average, do you examine on a six-month basis, Dr. Pashayan?" asked Nellis.

"Hundreds," the doctor replied.

"More than 500?" Nellis asked.

"Yes," the doctor replied.

"Would you say the same of Dr. Scott, since you work so close together?" asked Nellis.

"Yes, I suppose," answered Pashayan.

"Well, Dr. Pashayan, your memory and Dr. Scott's must be beyond human if you can recall such detail from every patient you examine, for such a long period of time," remarked Nellis, questioning the accuracy of the doctors' recollection.

"Objection!" said District Attorney Blessing. "Your Honor, I beg you to strike Mr. Nellis' last remarks from the record and ask Mr. Nellis to show some decorum towards the State's witness."

"Overruled," said Judge Van Kirk. "Mr. Nellis, please tone down your sarcasm."

"Yes, Your Honor," said Nellis.

"Doctor, how often did you contact the District Attorney regarding this case?" asked Nellis.

"I only contacted the District Attorney to relay the results of the examinations conducted on Mr. Pontón," said Pashayan.

"Do you recall how many times?" asked Nellis.

"No," said Pashayan.

"Dr. Pashayan, how often do you communicate with District Attorney Blessing on a regular basis?" asked Nellis.

"Often," the doctor responded. "I am contracted regularly to conduct examinations for the District Attorney," he answered.

"And so is Dr. Scott, I assume," Nellis asked.

"It is my understanding, yes," Pashayan answered.

"Doctor, in your opinion, how reliable are the blood tests used by the defense in this case to determine whether Mr. Pontón had syphillis?" asked Nellis.

"As reliable as any," answered the witness.

"To your knowledge, did you, Dr. Scott or the prosecution conduct any blood tests of Mr. Pontón?" asked Nellis.

"Not as far as I know," Pashayan responded.

"Dr. Pashayan, you had the opportunity to examine Mr. Pontón's lesions when they were presented to the jury, the judge and Dr. Scott moments ago. Are these lesions indicative of syphilis?" Nellis asked.

"The lesions might or might not indicate the disease, and it may be that under certain conditions they might indicate another infectious disease acquired through irregular habits," said Pashayan.

"Irregular habits? Like being confined in a prison cell with limited movement?" asked Nellis.

"Perhaps, or something else," Dr. Pashayan said.

"Like what?" asked Nellis.

"I would not know without further study," Dr. Pashayan said.

"Very well. Did you ask Mr. Pontón if he had a family history of mental illness, and if so, what did he say?" asked Nellis.

"Yes," Pashayan answered. "He mentioned that two cousins on his mother's side were insane."

"Thank you Doctor. No further questions for now," said Nellis.

After Nellis dismissed Dr. Pashayan, he recalled Coroner E. H. Jackson to the stand. His cross-examination showed that the evidence in Bessie Kromer's body corroborated Antonio's statements made to the *Schenectady Gazette* reporter while in the hospital, as to the nature of the sexual intimacy between Bessie and Antonio.

Nellis was careful not to drill down further on this subject, as the jury may perceive the questioning as improper, or as victim abuse. He did not ask Jackson to provide additional detail as to why he thought this was the case, including whether he found evidence of syphilis on Bessie's body.

District Attorney Blessing then called J. J. Cullen, the clerk at the Albany Hardware Company, who testified to selling the hunting knife to Antonio sometime in September of 1914.

Blessing then called for a recess.

As he walked escorted outside of the courtroom during recess, Antonio recognized Mr. Watson, the Albany Law School Registrar, and extended his hand at him to shake it. Watson took Antonio's hand but soon moved it away. It was evident that Antonio felt slighted by Watson, but he continued to greet law student friends that had come to court to support him.

Antonio was appreciative of the students' gesture.

Chapter 43. Closing Statements and Jury Instructions

T he matter went to the jury for deliberations on April 23, 1915 after closing statements by the defense and the prosecution. Former judge Andrew J. Nellis summed up for the defense. "Mr. Pontón was not in the right mind when he struck Miss Kromer. His was an impulsive act, without the thought of killing her."

Nellis read about a dozen letters written by Bessie to Antonio. The first letters showed that she was madly in love with Antonio and the last letters showed that her love grew cold, and that she wished to end the relationship.

"The proper representatives of the law accuse Pontón of having deliberately caused the death of Bessie Kromer, with premeditation and malice. You have seen him here, seen his lack of self-control. We assert that he killed Bessie Kromer on impulse, in a frenzy, as the dog bites the hand that caresses it. We feel that you should render a verdict of no cause of action because of insanity," Nellis said to the jury.

Nellis then sketched the first meeting of Bessie and Antonio the summer of 1911 and traced their relations from then on. "She sought the affections of the polished Spaniard, who soon became infatuated," he said. "Their letters breathed deep love on both sides for many months, and he continued to pour out his love and worship down to almost the very day of the tragedy."

Exhibiting the torn letter Antonio had written to Registrar Watson, found on Antonio's body the night of the murder, Attorney Nellis said, "It shows she was blowing hot and blowing cold, so that one day he contemplated suicide and the next he was raised to the heights of heaven." He suggested Antonio could not cope with the stress, especially in light of his deteriorated mental health.

Attorney Nellis used the statement made by Antonio to the

Schenectady Gazette reporter to show the intimacy between him and Bessie, rebutting the prosecution's opening statements and Mrs. Kromer's testimony that she did not know of the relationship between Antonio and Bessie.

"They stopped at hotels as man and wife. We have seen he went to Schoharie and into the Kromer family. This young woman once sought to win the affections of this young man. She wrote, *'Yo te amo.* I love you,' in his book and gave every indication that his approaches were not at all unwelcome. Thus, she began her intimacy with this member of a race which is, historically, not immoral, but unmoral," Nellis stated to the jury.

As he spoke of Antonio's race as "historically unmoral," Nellis introduced an element of racial bias against his own client that would backfire, with certainty. Instead of endearing the jurors to a defendant "who did not know better because of his race," as Nellis hoped to achieve with his statement, Nellis denigrated Antonio's race and with this, his client's life lost value before the jury.

Nellis' statement was a strong sign of the times, where racial, religious and other bias permeated throughout society in the United States, into the courtroom, past the guarding gargoyles of justice.

Showing the jurors the photograph of Bessie and Antonio together at Coney Island, Attorney Nellis said, "It has been shown they were together in the closest intimacy that can exist between a man and woman."

Contrary to what prosecutor Featherstonhaugh stated to the jury during his opening statement, Nellis showed that the evidence demonstrated that the couple's relationship was not based on mere friendship. Much to the contrary, there was a close, long-lasting romantic relationship, almost amounting to common-law marriage, which Mrs. Kromer did not support and wanted terminated.

After he proceeded to attack the testimony of the prosecution's insanity experts, pointing to the many inconsistencies, such as the doctors not taking notes and testifying from memory about examinations taken so long before the trial; their not advising Antonio about the purpose of their examination, so he could secure the advice of counsel; and that the doctors' examinations were not thorough, among other constitutional violations, Nellis concluded with a strong plea that Antonio's life should be spared.

"Antonio Pontón was insane at the time he committed the crime.

He did not know what he was doing was wrong! He does not deserve to be executed!" the defense lawyer closed.

Judge Van Kirk remained seated back on his bench. Most jurors seemed disconnected.

. . .

"There was not a bit of doubt that the Porto Rican had planned the crime," began District Attorney Blessing's closing.

He then read letters from Antonio to Bessie found in Bessie's room after her death. The letters showed that Bessie expressed she no longer wanted to see Antonio, and that he was on the verge of suicide.

In a dramatic spell, Blessing declared, "If there ever was an inexcusable, premeditated, deliberate, cold-blooded and damnable murder, you have it right here. If there ever was a deliberate, cold-blooded, vicious, cowardly murderer, that murderer sits right there. Sad was the day when he came into her life. In four short years her lifeblood was flowing in our street, murdered in cold blood. He ruined her fair name and stole her virtue under the false colors he called love, but which was nothing more, nor less, than the satisfying of his worse-than-brute passion. But that was not all. Not yet satisfied, instead of protecting that girl's honor, that would-be insane wretch gave out a statement revealing their relations and dragging down the girl's name."

Judge Van Kirk leaned forward on his bench, listening to Blessing. The jurors were mesmerized by Blessing's theatrical declarations.

Blessing then proceeded to read a letter from Bessie to Antonio, dated July 14, 1914, New York City, which Bessie called "the hardest letter she had ever written." The letter stated that they had acted like children; that they should stop before too late; that her love for him was lost when he first struck her. The letter said: "Go to your mother, tell her of striking me and your attempt to kill me." Another letter he read, dated August 3,1914, said Bessie never wanted to see Antonio again.

"The cold-blooded, deliberate act was as far from that of an insane man as is the east from the west," Blessing asserted.

The jurors' attention was fixed on Blessing, and so was everyone else's in the courtroom, including Judge Van Kirk's.

Blessing felt assured the verdict would be guilty, as charged.

. . .

Once the prosecution rested, Judge C. C. Van Kirk proceeded to give the jury instructions. "You should approach the evidence with the innocence of the defendant presumed, and you should not hold against the defendant the fact that he did not take the stand," the judge stated to the jurors.

He then explained the degrees of homicide. Judge Van Kirk told the jury that the charge of *murder in the first degree* required premeditation and was punishable by death, unless excused.

Under the strict *M'Naghten Rule*, codified into New York law, a criminal defendant would not be excused except upon proof that, at the time of committing the alleged criminal act, he was laboring under such a defect of reason as not to know the nature and quality of the act he was doing; or not to know that the act was wrong.

The judge continued explaining. *Murder in the second degree* did not require premeditation and was punishable by imprisonment from 20 years to life.

Judge Van Kirk then explained the two degrees of *manslaughter* or accidental death, and their corresponding punishment, and concluded with a definition of *excusable homicide* and *justifiable homicide*, lesser offenses where the act caused an unintended or justifiable death.

Van Kirk told the jurors, "There is no doubt that Mr. Pontón has syphilis in his blood."

"But," he said, "The one thing is, does he or does he not have syphilitic insanity? We have had no direct testimony here that this man was in a condition of mind where he did not know the difference between right and wrong," the judge instructed the jury, ignoring the evidence of neurosyphilis presented and the testimony of hereditary insanity offered by the defense.

To the defense's astonishment, the Judge improperly added a swaying statement of opinion. He told the jury there was no testimony offered by the defense to excuse Antonio. None. But it was not his place to make such a judgment. Whether there was enough evidence of insanity or not was the jury's *issue of fact* to determine, not the judge's.

Van Kirk had committed a terrible error.

"It is your duty to give to the defendant as fair and honest a trial as you can give him," the judge continued, oblivious that what he had just done violated his own instruction of fairness and honesty. "If you have an honest doubt as to whether this crime has been proven within the degrees I have stated to you, you must give him the benefit of that doubt: but you must not entertain a doubt for the sole purpose of avoiding a disagreeable duty, or a doubt on any other ground than because the evidence justifies it," the judge said.

On April 23, 1915 at 12:30 p.m., the case went to the jury for deliberations.

Chapter 44. Verdict and Sentence

Antonio waited for the verdict in the detention room, close to the courtroom, with his guard Deputy Sheriff E. C. Finkle. After lunch, Miguel de la Rosa joined Antonio in his wait.

About 6:00 p.m. Jury Foreman Charles B. Cox contacted the Court stating that the jury had a question. Everyone was summoned back to the courtroom.

Antonio's anxiety was apparent. At the defendant's table, he was shaking his right leg and sweating, being consoled by de la Rosa.

"*Antonio, ¡Eso no es tan malo!* It is not so bad! The jury having a question means that they are giving the evidence some thought. That they are thinking about everything. It is not so bad," said de la Rosa.

All seated in the courtroom, Foreman Cox then stated to the court, "The jurors want to know how much time is required for premeditation."

Judicial precedent in *People v. Conroy*, 153 N.Y. 174 (1897), stated that premeditation "is always a question for the jury in light of the facts." *People v. Jackson*, 196 N.Y. 357 (1909), stated that for the jury to find premeditation, the jurors would have to find that the intent to kill must have existed for some period before the slaying, and *it could not take place in a fraction of a second or at the moment of striking the fatal blow.*

Justice Van Kirk replied to Cox, "Premeditation requires time enough for conscious resolve. It could be a minute or it might be longer. No specific period of time is required."

But the judge did not tell the jury that premeditation cannot take a fraction of a second or occur at the moment of striking the fatal blow, as stated by *Conroy*. This would have made a difference as the jury debated the issue. The jurors were clearly considering the lesser charge.

The life of a man depended on the accuracy of the court's

definition.

The life of a human being.

Van Kirk asked, "When will the jury come up with a decision, Mr. Cox?"

"Not long, Your Honor. Not long," said Cox.

All returned to their respective waiting areas.

. . .

At 6:35 p.m. on a Friday, the same day of the week and at the exact hour at which Antonio Pontón ended Bessie Kromer's life, the jury announced they were ready to return a verdict. Antonio was called back to the courtroom, accompanied by his lawyers, Deputy Sheriff Finkle and family friend de la Rosa.

"All rise!" said the court crier.

"Has the jury reached a verdict?" the judge asked Foreman Cox.

"Yes, Your Honor. We have," replied Cox.

Cox paused.

"What is your verdict?" said the judge.

Antonio could not bear the tension. Drops of sweat rained down his forehead. His knees weak. His hands sweaty. He was light-headed and on the verge of collapse.

Mrs. Kromer fixed her gaze on Antonio and held her son Charles' hand with great force.

"Guilty of murder in the first degree, as charged," stated Jury Foreman Cox.

A cry, almost in scream of agony, burst from Antonio.

"No! This cannot be! I loved her! I could not have killed her! I don't remember killing her. Please, no!"

The defense lawyers tried to comfort Antonio as the courtroom burst into noisy exclamations and commentary.

"Mr. Pontón, we will ask for a new trial, and if not granted, we will appeal. Remember what we discussed?" said Borst to his client, who had crumbled down on the defendant's table.

"This is not over, Mr. Pontón. You will have another chance," said Nellis, patting Antonio's back in sign of support.

Antonio calmed down some, but he continued drying sweat from his face with his wrinkled handkerchief.

Mrs. Kromer showed no emotion whatsoever at the verdict, but from her face permeated the excruciating pain of a mother who had lost her daughter and sought retribution. The verdict was not going to bring Bessie back, but she wanted Antonio to pay.

And she got the conviction she wanted.

The crowd's bickering could be heard in the background. People were divided in their opinions about the outcome. Many women showed satisfaction at the verdict. "Let him fry!" they cried, while others expressed the death penalty was not the solution for Antonio. "He should not be executed! The man was obviously insane!" they said.

"If you doubt premeditation, then you have reasonable doubt. The jury doubted premeditation. There was enough testimony to suspect insanity! There was reasonable doubt! This is wrong!" Antonio's law school classmates stated out loud in protest.

Judge Van Kirk struck his gavel.

"Order in the court!" the judge demanded, striking the gavel again.

The officers helped him by waving their hands signaling to the crowd the court was still in session.

When the courtroom background noise dissipated, defense attorney Homer Borst moved to dismiss. "Your Honor, the defense moves to dismiss the verdict on the grounds that it is contrary to the facts and the evidence. The defense requests a new trial," he said.

The court denied the pre-sentence motion.

"The State moves for sentencing at this time, Your Honor," said District Attorney Blessing.

Antonio was directed to go to the clerk's desk and give his record. He stood up, still in disbelief at the verdict, and he prepared to follow the judge's instructions. Antonio addressed the court in low tones, gaining his composure, and aided by Manuel de la Rosa and Deputy Sheriff Finkle.

"Name?" said the clerk.

"Antonio Pontón," he replied.

Age: 28 years

Parents: Manuel and Etervina. Living.

Birthplace: Comerío, Puerto Rico

Residence: The Same

Religion: Roman Catholic

Criminal History: Never convicted of a crime before.

"Mr. Pontón, have you anything to say why sentence should not be passed upon you?" asked Judge Van Kirk.

A shaking Antonio read a statement his lawyers had prepared to assist him:

"When Dr. Scott and Dr. Pashayan came to the jail they did not tell me they were doctors and did not tell me who they came for or that what I said would be given to the district attorney. They did not strip me or examine me below the waist. They did not try me with the hot-and-cold water test to see if I felt pain, as they said. They did not examine my throat as they said they did. They did not examine my eyes as the said they did. They took a lot of notes as they were making the examinations, but they said in court they did not. Dr. Jackson examined my eyes out there in the corridor the other day and found I had the *Argyll Robinson* pupil."

The *Argyll Robinson Pupil* Antonio referred to was a term of art, still used today to describe a pupil that reduces in size when a patient focuses on a near object, but does not constrict when exposed to bright light. This type of pupil is a highly specific sign of *neurosyphilis* and was and remains a "cardinal sign" of the disease. A patient with the *Argyll Robinson Pupil* was clinically considered to have dementia induced by the damage caused by the syphilis invasion of the brain.

After he read the statement, Antonio, on his own, showed his right ankle to the judge and displayed what he claimed was a scar. But there was nothing there. He told the judge it was made by a burn when his father allegedly branded him with a hot iron.

Antonio's lawyers looked at each other with surprise as to why Antonio had made this statement. Antonio's delusions were increasingly overcoming him.

"There is nothing on his ankle. He must have imagined it," Borst told Smith as they returned to the defendant's table with their client. "The judge has to know this man is insane. It's right in front of him!"

The Judge then spoke to Antonio.

"Pontón, you are an intelligent man, who knew what you were doing," said Van Kirk, resolute.

The judge had just uttered the elements of the crime of murder in the first degree, warranting the death penalty, under New York law.

On April 23, 1915 at 6:35 p.m., Antonio Pontón became the first Puerto Rican convicted of murder outside the island and the first Puerto Rican and Hispanic to be sentenced to die on the electric chair in the United States.

He also became the first man convicted to die by electric

execution in Schenectady County in 24 years. The last man sent to the electric chair in Schenectady County was Carmel Loth, convicted of murder in the first degree for the brutal killing of a woman. He had crushed her head with an axe, cut her throat with a butcher knife and slashed the entire length of the body trunk.

Justice Van Kirk scheduled the week of June 7, 1915 and Sing Sing prison as the time and place of Antonio's execution.

The judge signaled the end of the trial. The court crier asked those in the room to rise. Silent, all present in the courtroom stood up and waited for the judge to exit.

Antonio watched Van Kirk disappear through the back door behind his bench, located under the sign that read "Equal Justice Under Law."

Van Kirk floated away, like a ghost.

The court clerks then asked everyone to vacate the courtroom, and the crowd began to dissipate as Deputy Sheriff Finkle prepared to escort Antonio back to jail.

Antonio was scheduled for transport to Sing Sing Prison the next day.

Chapter 45. Smoke, Mirrors and Costs

The *Albany Evening Journal* published an editorial on April 24, 1915, the day after Antonio's verdict. It read: "The jury has set a good example. The plea of insanity, made on behalf of a person whose sanity was never questioned until he committed the crime of murder, and never would have been questioned unless he had committed it, has been too often effective to avert from a murderer the penalty of the law. ... Public opinion will approve."

The editorial omitted Antonio's family history of insanity, his deteriorating mental health, and the evidence presented at trial regarding his illness.

It is not difficult to sway public opinion. So many are averse to the employment of checks and balances before passing judgment.

. . .

The cost to the State of New York for Antonio's trial was $2,983.56, from which a good portion went to the prosecution's expert witnesses. The Supreme Court, Judge Van Kirk presiding, allowed a payment of $400 to Dr. Pashayan and of $400 to Dr. Scott for their expert testimony on behalf of the prosecution. The judge allowed $562 to Homer J. Borst for defending Antonio Pontón, which would be split among Borst, Smith and Nellis, and it denied the request of $225 by Dr. Charles Bailey, alienist for the defense. The judge also denied the charge of $35 by Dr. Ellis Kellert for performing a blood test on Antonio Pontón. He did authorize $10 for witness fees, instead. The remaining expense went to juror per diem, stenographer, printing, witnesses, and court crier and officers.

Chapter 46. Verdict Disparities: Harry K. Thaw

T he verdict in Antonio Pontón's murder trial contrasted with that in the Harry K. Thaw murder case, where the defendant also pled insanity. The press reported about the Pontón and Thaw criminal matters side-by-side on the April 23, 1915 issue of the *Albany Evening Journal*, but never commented on the different outcomes of the cases.

Multimillionaire heir Harry K. Thaw was the son of William Thaw, Sr., the Pittsburgh coal and railroad baron, and heir to a multi-million dollar mine and railroad fortune. Young Thaw had a history of a troubled and disorderly life. His family had enormous wealth, by far much greater than Antonio's father Manuel Pontón could possible amass. Harry Thaw was able to buy pretty much anything and anyone, except for his law degree at Harvard University. The prestigious institution expelled him for his moral turpitude.

Thaw bought the affections of cabaret dancer Evelyn Nesbit, who ended up marrying him, even though she admitted Thaw had beaten her with a whip and raped her during an Austrian trip the couple took together early in their relationship. Prior to meeting Thaw, when she was only 16, Nesbit had an affair with millionaire architect Stanford White, many years her elder. White remained interested in Nesbit, even after their breakup. In fact, upon learning of Nesbit's misfortunes with Thaw, White hired lawyers to help her out of her relationship with Thaw. After Nesbit decided not to press charges and ended up marrying Thaw, White also moved on, married and had a family.

However, the hatred Thaw harbored against White exacerbated when Nesbit confessed to Thaw that White had defiled her against her will when they first met. On June 25, 1906, in a jealous rage, Thaw planned the shooting and murder of White, which Thaw carried out on the roof of the Madison Square Garden, surrounded by a mass of witnesses. Harry Thaw shot White three times.

When Thaw's arresting officer asked him, "Why did you kill him?" Thaw responded, "He ruined my wife," admitting to having a motive for the killing.

Thaw's first murder trial on April 1907 resulted in a hung jury; the press reported that the outcome was secured by Thaw's bribing of a juror with $100,000. The vast majority of the testimony offered at trial pointed to Thaw's sanity.

The Lunacy Commission impaneled for Thaw's second trial stated: "Upon all of the facts it is our opinion that at the time of our examination the said Harry K. Thaw was and is sane and was not and is not in a state of idiocy, imbecility, lunacy, or insanity so as to be incapable of rightly understanding his own condition, the nature of the charges against him, and of conducting his defense in a rational manner."

However, rebuttal testimony was offered in support of his insanity. Thaw's mother testified that her son was hurt by a "prenatal episode" that caused him to have an abnormal mental capacity. Dr. Bailey, the same defense expert witness Antonio Pontón's lawyers summoned, also testified in favor of Thaw's insanity, and so did the family physician, Dr. C. C. Wiley.

The defense's creative theory was *"Dementia Americana,"* a made-up mix of justifiable homicide and insanity theory, representing that Thaw suffered a sudden bout of insanity grounded on American moral values. This type of dementia compelled him to right the past wrong White had committed years prior against Thaw's now wife, when she was only 16 years old.

Although Thaw was tried under the same law as Antonio Pontón had, and the facts of Thaw's case pointed to a much clearer premeditation, deliberate intent and motive to kill, on February 1, 1908 Thaw's attorneys succeeded in securing a verdict favoring their client's insanity defense.

The price tag for Thaw's legal fees was estimated at over $250,000, excluding other expenses.

Harry Thaw was sent to the Matteawan Asylum for the Criminally Insane in Fishkill, New York. There, he tried to secure his release by bribing the asylum's director with $25,000 in exchange for stating that Thaw was cured. The director accepted. However, the bribery was discovered, and the director and the lawyer who negotiated the bribe were charged with bribery.

In court, Thaw testified that the lawyer was working for the doctor, not him, and the money was an administrative payment the asylum director requested from Thaw as part of his "discharge fees." While he testified to the bribery charge, Thaw refused to answer any questions regarding his intent to murder White. Thaw was well aware of his constitutional rights and responded that the murder was not the reason why he was called to testify, and therefore he would not answer the irrelevant question.

It was not a surprise that Thaw was exonerated from all bribery charges. The asylum director was fired, and the lawyer who negotiated the bribe was cleared of charges upon return of the money to Thaw.

Not long after this episode, Thaw arranged with some friends to help his escape from the insane asylum to Canada. Once there, Thaw was deported back to the United States, where he filed a *habeas corpus* petition to the court to be declared sane and released from the asylum. In 1915, around the time Antonio Pontón's trial was taking place, a court allowed a jury to decide the issue of Thaw's insanity. The jury decided that Thaw was cured, and he was set free.

Thaw was indicted again on January of 1917, eleven months after his court-sanctioned release from the asylum, for the kidnapping and assault of a young boy with a whip. Thaw had lured the boy, Frederick Gump, to a hotel in New York with promises of paying for his education abroad. Gump, a minor, testified Thaw used his bodyguard to subdue and molest him and to compel him not to speak about the incident. Afterwards, Gump was able to break free and went home to his parents. He then told his story and showed his wounds to the authorities. Witnesses reported that Thaw often beat and whipped young girls until they bled, as he had done Gump.

Soon after he was arrested and indicted, Thaw attempted suicide by slashing his wrists and was admitted to the hospital, where he spent six weeks, his mother by his side. Thaw's mother then initiated independent proceedings to declare him insane, in an effort to free him from criminal prosecution and incarceration.

Examinations revealed that a cousin and an uncle of Thaw's had histories of mental illness, similar to the situation with Antonio's family, except that Antonio's family history of mental illness included many more individuals. In addition, Mrs. Thaw settled out of court with Gump in a civil matter he had filed against her son Harry. The settlement was documented to be for an amount under $100,000.

Thaw spent seven years in an insane asylum, and in 1924 he requested to the court once again to be declared sane. He was eventually found sane by a jury impaneled to determine the issue of his sanity, and he was released on April of 1924. Thaw never faced trial for the Gump matter, because Gump, by then married and with children, would not testify against Thaw, per their settlement agreement.

After his release, Thaw went on to live an extravagant and wasteful life, the term "playboy" being coined after him.

Harry K. Thaw's great wealth and high social status purchased his freedom every step of the way. Many saw him as a narcissistic sociopath and the spoiled product of being given everything throughout his life. Thaw died of a heart attack at the age of 76 in Florida.

The disparity of outcomes in Antonio Pontón's and Harry K. Thaw's cases is disturbing. Thaw had the financial resources and societal position to openly purchase people, mock the authorities, manipulate the courts, and ultimately secure his freedom. Antonio, a "Porto Rican immigrant" who lacked the practical understanding of his constitutional rights in the United States, rights still unclear to many in the United States and Puerto Rico, did not have the social status and the supreme wealth to accomplish what Thaw had, which enabled Thaw to escape the ultimate punishment not only once, but twice.

When comparing the Harry Thaw and Antonio Pontón cases, it becomes evident that the principle of "Equal Justice Under Law" was applied arbitrarily. Contrary to the *Magna Carta*'s basic tenets of the American Justice System, stating that justice should not be sold to anyone, justice was indeed purchased by the Thaw fortune.

Part V. To Sing Sing

"In Sing Sing Prison, in a ghastly white room stands a chair. Its parts are heavy joinings of oak, riveted and screwed together; its strong legs fastened to the floor with teeth and claws of steel. It bites into the marrow of men with fangs of fire. For this is the faldstool of bloody human justice, the prayer-chair of man's vengeance upon man. Into it are strapped ... men who have killed other men. In it, for a high moral purpose, erring human lives are shocked across the barrier into night and the grave."

- Edward H. Smith (1918)

Chapter 47. Journey to Sing Sing Prison

The morning of April 27, 1915, Sheriff Welch left Schenectady Jail for Sing Sing Prison with Antonio Pontón. The prisoner gave his farewells to the guards and to Mrs. Welch, who had treated him with much kindness during his stay there.

Taken to Albany via automobile, Antonio boarded the 9:40 a.m. train to Ossining, escorted by Sheriff Welch, Roy Welch and Under Sheriff Russell R. Hunt. They arrived in Sing Sing at 1 o'clock and entered the office of Receiving Clerk Westlake.

Although he was calm through his journey to Sing Sing, during the check-in process at the receiving office the reality of his fate sank in, and Antonio began showing signs of collapse. As he filled out the processing documents, his hand was shaking.

The *Sing Sing Receiving Blotter* form called for general information about a prisoner: his name, his charge, his conviction and date, his profession, former address, nationality, religion, as well as some physical information. The form also asked for a prisoner's closest personal contact. In this line, Antonio wrote, with the greatest of hopes: "*Cousin, Luis Muñoz Rivera, Congressman, Washington, D.C.*" and he signed at the bottom of the form.

When Sheriff Welch turned to leave, Antonio broke down, embraced him and wept. Between sobs, Antonio offered the sheriff a farewell and uttered short, broken sentences regarding his nearing death.

"Is this the last time we will see each other, Sheriff?" asked Antonio.

"Mr. Pontón, your lawyers will continue to try to save your life," said the Sheriff. "I am sure we will meet again," said the Sheriff, trying to comfort the prisoner.

Antonio did not know the Sheriff was required to be a witness in his execution, if it ever took place. Welch would see him again, one way or another. He clung to the sheriff with such force that two guards had to wrench him loose. The press reported that he was "forcibly, but gently taken away," and speculated about his state of mind, stating his feelings were "probably of mingled grief, at parting for the last time with a man who had been a friend during the many previous weeks of confinement, and fear of what awaited him."

"It's pretty hard to be put in here," Antonio told Sheriff Welch as he was being escorted away. "I haven't been in trouble before."

"I know, Mr. Pontón. But you must be strong," said Welch, trying to encourage him.

When separated from Welch, Antonio was carried down to the reception room and then to the *Death House*. At the time of his arrival in Sing Sing, he was the 19th prisoner there awaiting execution. Besides him, there were 15 men and 3 women.

. . .

The Sing Sing Correctional Facility is a maximum-security prison located about 30 miles north of New York City on the east bank of the Hudson River. Due to its location the locals refer to Sing Sing as the place "up the river." The prison got its name from the *Sint Sink* Indians. The term means "stone upon stone."

Built by inmates, Sing Sing's construction began in 1825 on the site of an abandoned quarry. In 1915, it contained about 1,200 tomblike cells encased in stone masonry, about 3'3"x 7' x 6'7" in size. At the time Antonio arrived, the prison property housed the main prisoner population (non-death-row) separate from those inmates condemned to die on the electric chair. The *Death House*, a smaller prison inside of the prison, housed the death row inmates.

The *Death House* back then was a self-contained unit, with its own hospital, kitchen, exercise yard and visiting room. The cells were inadequate, dark, and did not have proper sanitary facilities or ventilation. One window and skylight furnished the ventilation and light of the entire unit. Twelve cells were on the lower tier, six on each side, facing each other, with a narrow corridor between them. Five cells were located in an upper tier. There was an area the prisoners called the *Dance Hall* that housed a prisoner to be executed on his last day. The narrow corridor connected the *Dance Hall* to the execution room, where the *Electric Chair* resided. The prisoners named this corridor the *Last Mile* or the *Green Mile*, because this was the last walk a prisoner would take all the way to the small green riveted door at the end of the corridor, on his way to the execution room.

. . .

Upon his arrival at Sing Sing, Antonio passed through a process known as *dressing in*. As part of this process, a keeper asked him questions and took a personal history of the case. The convict then surrendered his clothing and whatever possessions he had with him. He then took a bath, put in his new prison clothing and was locked in a cell in the reception section. His new uniform was muddy brown, and this distinguished him from the uniform the rest of the inmates wore, which was military gray. He wore this brown uniform until the quarantine period passed.

For about two weeks, the new prisoner remained alone in his cell, except for about an hour each day, dedicated to physical and mental examinations and training on prison life. During this time the *Sing Sing Doctor* developed a medical treatment profile for the inmate. Also, psychologists and psychiatrists learned about the inmate's mind and determined the possible source of his criminal behavior.

Dr. Amos O. Squire became Chief Physician at Sing Sing in 1914. He was born in 1876 in Cold Spring, New York. Before he began his medical studies at Columbia University in 1895, he took a job as a public school teacher, walking seven miles from his home to his place of employment. This job helped him pay for medical school. He graduated from Columbia University in 1899. After his medical residence, he was a prison consultant, later becoming Sing Sing's Chief Physician when the position became available. Dr. Squire retired in 1925, having participated in 138 executions. Many prisoners liked him. His public lectures educated participants about criminals and their potential rehabilitation from a medical perspective.

A gray-haired man with a full oval face, a dimple on his square chin, and a groomed short moustache, Squire was a knowledgeable and compassionate man, and a firm opponent of the death penalty. After he became the Westchester County Medical Examiner, he wrote about his experiences at Sing Sing in his book *Sing Sing Doctor*, which he published in 1935.

According to Dr. Squire, after joining the Sing Sing population, death row inmates received medical attention every day and kept healthy, such that "the law was not cheated of its extreme penalty." As many of them received reprieves even minutes before execution, this medical care was appropriate. However, if a prisoner faced a situation that may cause him death before his execution, he had a choice to get treated for it, or not.

. . .

For one hour in the morning and one hour in the afternoon Antonio Pontón and the other prisoners were let out of their cages to the *Death House* yard for a breath of fresh air. The yard was a long quadrangle measuring about 60 x 20 feet and was enclosed on three sides by brick walls. The fourth side was faced by the windows of the principal keeper's office, which were protected by iron bars. The inmates could exercise, rest, talk with each other, and play games if they wished.

"Hey, new guy! What are you in for?" asked a young prisoner during Antonio's first walk outside.

"I am told I killed my girlfriend, but I don't remember," said Antonio. "And you?"

"They tell me I killed two police officers and a gangster, but 'I don't remember' either!" said Oresto Shillitoni, the gangster, laughing while winking at the other prisoners.

The prisoners chuckled.

"And he, the one pacing over there, the quiet-looking guy," Shillitoni pointed. "He killed his girlfriend, too. She was pregnant! And wait, it gets better!" said Shillitoni, mocking Hans Schmidt. "He is a priest! He cut her into pieces and threw her body in the river. Nice fella, huh?"

Antonio was stunned at what he though was one of the most monstrous deeds he had ever heard of, unaware of the gruesomeness of his own.

"And that one is a rozzer," Shillitoni continued, pointing to ex-police officer Charles Becker, who was sitting down by himself. "He's here for taking down Herman Rosenthal, a high-roller. Becker had a good thing going, ya know. He had a protection racket with whorehouses and gambling houses. I guess Rosenthal didn't wanna pay up anymore, and bham! He got it good! The poor bastard!"

Antonio looked down, silent, as Shillitoni kept talking. There he was, among cold-blooded killers, talking to a gangster. A much different picture than a year prior.

"Can't trust priests, can't trust cops either. Can't trust nobody! Whaddaya say?"

"I am not like you," Antonio said. "I'm not like them, either. That's what I say. I am not a cold-blooded killer!"

"Ya killed, you a killa! There's not'ng more to it!" Shillitoni said.

Antonio had no response.

"They say ya'll get used to it," Shillitoni said. "But I won't. I'm gonna get out of here. These bastards won't fry me!"

"*Fried* ... I heard that before," Antonio thought. But he said nothing to Shillitoni. It was not worth it.

"Time's up," said George B. Meserole, the prison guard. "You ladies have another chance to chit-chat after lunch!"

Shillitoni escaped Sing Sing prison on June 22, 1916 with no clothes on. He was recaptured and executed on June 30th.

. . .

Lunch consisted of fried potatoes, bread, meat (or, as the prisoners called it, "horse meat"), dried peaches and coffee or tea (which the prisoner would have to purchase from the prison's store, if they wanted.) Some prisoners did not have any means for money, so they went without the luxury of coffee or tea, unless someone exercised some charity and purchased it for them. The store would also sell tobacco, fruit, and other groceries, but the inmates could only purchase a maximum of $6 in groceries per month.

During the afternoon, the men read, slept, smoked, talked or prayed.

At first, Antonio slept most of the time while at his cell. But on occasion he would awaken from a nightmare, weeping. It was not unusual for prisoners to weep from time to time, in particular after the execution of a fellow inmate.

"Shut up!" a prisoner shouted at Antonio.

"Boo!" other prisoners yelled at him. "Man up!"

"Pontón, calm down my friend," a soothing voice came from another cell. "You are bringing down everyone's spirits! Everyone is trying to make it 'til the end, here. A fellow's crying does not help the rest of us!"

"I'm sory," said Antonio. "I can't control myself. This is horribehl!"

The prisoners tried to keep a positive attitude, given the gloomy circumstances surrounding their destiny. But this was a daunting task, eased in part at the prisoner's option by talking to Father Cashin, the resident prison chaplain since 1912.

Father William E. Cashin (b 1872) was an Irish Catholic priest who was convinced that there was "more loyalty, sympathy and understanding within the walls of the prison than in any other place of equal area." The priest attended to about 150 executions before he was reassigned to St. Andrew's Church in New York in 1924. Father Cashin would stop by the *Death House* during the afternoons to visit, and many men found much relief in his company. His visit calmed Antonio and the other prisoners when an electrocution neared, and above all, after the horrific event.

Chapter 48. The Terror Surrounding the Death House

During the day, Antonio Pontón waited in bright light as the sunlight streamed in from the glass roof into the *Death House*, but then came the nights.

In darkness, Antonio prayed alone, on his knees, as many of the other death row inmates, hoping for Heaven's interference with his terrene fate. He prayed for a second chance, for the terror surrounding the *Death House* to stop.

The arrangement of cells in the *Death House* was barbaric. The execution room, the *White Room*, was too close to the rest of the cells. On execution day, a condemned man had to walk by the cells of other prisoners, through the narrow corridor, through the *Green Door*, and into the *White Room*. This door was only a few feet from the cells housing the other condemned. The men could not only hear with detail the terrible sounds of what went on in the execution chamber, behind the green riveted door, but also what went on afterwards in the adjacent autopsy room.

The law required that an autopsy be performed after each electrocution. As part of this procedure, the *Sing Sing Chief Physician* would remove the top of the executed man's skull with a saw to examine his brain. To the men in the condemned cells, who were already tortured by witnessing their fellow condemned men walk by them and pass through the *Green Door*, the most horrible thing was to hear the sound of that saw, screeching and whining while cutting through the skull of a man who minutes earlier had a pulse.

Due to the stressful environment, to prevent suicide, *Death House* rules forbade any outside food, books, newspapers or similar items, where tools to aid in suicide could be concealed. The prison library was the sole source of reading material. Food was prepared in a kitchen located within the *Death House*. Since no knives or forks were

210

allowed, the food was chopped before serving so that it could be eaten with a spoon. The guard would count the spoons and plates at the end of every meal.

The prison doctor could not use narcotics to numb the person to be electrocuted prior to his walking to the execution room. However humane this might sound, the prison policy was that the deterrent effect of the execution would disappear if a condemned man were numbed. He was to be in possession of all his faculties when meeting death. If prior to walking to his execution a man were on the verge of collapse, the doctor gave him stimulants to wake him up. This was the law.

Dr. Amos O. Squire, Chief Sing Sing Physician, wrote that the terror of the execution increased day by day as the time neared. Many men in this situation acted as though they were in a daze, hypnotized, losing all regard for what was to be done to them. Some became delirious, others in acute hysteria. The doctor said that this was a way of the mind to cope with the terror. Some men on the electric chair had fainted between the time when the electrodes were placed on them and the time right before the throwing of the switch, so when the switch was thrown they were already unconscious. The doctor would not interfere when this happened. He would let the condemned die in that state.

. . .

Charles F. Stielow, a Sing Sing death row inmate like Antonio Pontón, was an illiterate farm worker, the father of three small children, married to an illiterate woman, a man of poor means with no friends. For Stielow, the solitude was even harsher. He had been convicted to death for a crime he did not commit. The days and nights were longer for Stielow, as he could not even read a book or write his thoughts down to ease the despair of the injustice cast upon him.

"I guess the worst is your thoughts and the way you're scared of *that door* and *The Chair*. But that ain't much worse than the way it's always the same," he said to Antonio when he arrived at Sing Sing. "The food's the same, so the men get so sick of it they throw it on the floor or sling it at the keepers. The hours is the same, the days is the same. Everything is the same. Always the same. It's awful." Stielow said that this somewhat changed when a fellow inmate's execution neared. "Then every man in the cells was alive and alert to the crisis of his fellow doomsman. Would the man be saved? Would a reprieve come? Would the sentence be commuted? Or must he die beyond the door?"

"There is hope for a reprieve?" Antonio asked.

"There is always hope for a reprieve, my friend," Stielow said. "You have to get the governor to pardon you if the courts fail on you. This is an unlikely thing, although possible. The last thing you hold on to 'til the last second is hope. Hope is what keeps us doomsmen sane, for the most part. A miracle."

During the eight months Antonio was at Sing Sing, he witnessed 13 men walk the *Green Mile* and endured the torturous sounds and smells of their electrocution and autopsy.

Chapter 49. Codifying Death

N ew York law specified in excruciating detail how death had to be administered, who could be present at an execution, when should they be invited, and who was responsible to coordinate witness invitations. It also described how the executed person's corpse would be examined and disposed of after the execution, up to the time of release to relatives or burial in he prison's graveyard.

The *New York Code of Criminal Procedure, Title X, Chapter I § 505 (1915),* dictated that the current had to be applied for as long as it took for a human to die. *"Death penalty; mode of infliction. The punishment of death must, in every case, be inflicted by causing to pass through the body of the convict, a current of electricity of sufficient intensity to cause death, and the application of such current must be continued until such convict is dead,"* the law stated.

The *New York Code of Criminal Procedure, Title X, Chapter I § 507 (1915),* defined in detail the execution protocol. It stated:

"Death penalty; who to be present. It is the duty of the agent and warden to be present at the execution, and to invite the presence, by at least three days' previous notice, of a justice of the supreme court, the district attorney, and the sheriff of the county where the conviction was had, together with two physicians and twelve reputable citizens of full age, to be selected by said agent and warden. Such agent and warden must, at the request of the criminal, permit such ministers of the gospel, priests or clergymen of any religious denomination, not exceeding two, to be present at the execution; and in addition to the persons designated above, he shall also appoint seven assistants or deputy sheriffs who shall attend the execution. He shall permit no other person to be present at such execution except those designated in this section. After the execution a post mortem

examination of the body of the convict shall be made by the physicians present at the execution and their report in writing stating the nature of the examination, so made by them, shall be annexed to the certificate hereinafter mentioned and filed therewith. After such post-mortem examination, the body, unless claimed by some relative or relatives of the person so executed, shall be interred in the graveyard or cemetery attached to the prison, with a sufficient quantity of quick-lime to consume such body without delay; and no religious or other services shall be held over the remains after such execution, except within the walls of the prison where said execution took place, and only in the presence of the officers of said prison, the person conducting said services and the immediate family and relatives of said deceased prisoner. Any person who shall violate or omit to comply with any provision of this section shall be guilty of a misdemeanor."

A society that condemned killing, ruled mostly by people who claimed to be of the highest religious beliefs, had codified how it would kill a human being, and how it would punish those who violated the killing code.

The hypocrisy.

Chapter 50. The Chair

I n 1916, employees of Thomas Edison's General Electric, Inc. in Schenectady manufactured the electric chair, the switchboard and other electrical equipment in the execution chamber. The board's design allowed the selection of predetermined shocks with a given voltage and amperage. The switchboard was set behind a screen, away from *The Chair*, to be maneuvered by the executioner or *electrician* during the *electrocution*, the term the businessmen coined for the *electric execution* of a human being. Wires carried the current from the switchboard to the electrodes to be placed on both the skull and right leg calf of the condemned, sometimes pre-shaven for the occasion.

The Chair was built at the suggestion of eccentric dentist Alfred P. Southwich, who was a member of a New York commission established in 1881 to determine "a more humane method of execution" to replace hanging. Southwich's suggestion was inspired by the case of a drunken man who had died right after touching exposed cables.

Thomas Edison's employees, Harold P. Brown and Arthur Kennelly, designed *The Chair* and suggested the use of *Alternating Current* (AC) as the most "lethal" current to be used for the device. The use of AC was a marketing ploy by Edison, who favored *Direct Current* (DC), to discredit his competitor Westinghouse, who used AC. Edison's idea was to associate AC with lethality, so that the government would adopt DC, Edison's favored current, as the preferred option for infrastructure development.

To demonstrate that AC was indeed lethal, Brown and Kennelly endeavored on an "animal electrocution spree" in Edison's laboratory. They paid children a quarter for each dog they brought to them for their "tests." They also electrocuted two horses and six calves during the testing to show that the process was painless and immediate, and thus adequate as a new method for "a more humane" execution.

Despite much polarity on the matter, in 1888 the legislature passed *The Electric Execution Law*, and in 1889 the New York Commission adopted the *AC electric chair.*

Dr. Amos O. Squire, Sing Sing Chief Physician, described the electric chair in his own words:

"The chair is secured to the floor, it is made of wood, varnished a dark brown, and is low, solid and angular. It has arms, a high back, and is tilted slightly toward the rear. Behind, it has two legs, but in front, a broad baseboard curves inward on either side to form a single wide center leg, upon which are attached two ankle grips. There are eight straps of heavy black harness leather, with buckles–for chest, waist, each upper arm, each forearm, and each ankle, the last two serving to hold the ankles in the grips. On the upper part of the back is fastened a flat, verticle [sic] headrest that can be adjusted. This headrest and the seat are faced with rubber matting."

. . .

The physiological effects of an electrocution are severe and painful. Besides launching the body into violent convulsions, the electrocution of a human being causes massive destruction throughout the body. Low voltages of AC cause ventricular defibrillation in the heart. Almost always, the heart's walls would rupture. High voltages of up to 2,000 volts damage the central nervous system triggering loss of consciousness and respiratory failure, at some point. The heavy current transforms into heat and destroys the brain by "cooking it." Sometimes the veins burst and the eyes melt. There have been reports of the head or a limb catching on fire, or the flesh burning down to the bone where the electrodes were placed.

The first electric execution occurred in 1890 at the Auburn Prison in New York. William Kemmler, an alcoholic, was convicted for killing his girlfriend with an axe after a dispute. During his electrocution, Kemmler turned bright red and went into convulsions, but surprisingly, he did not die. Kemmler appeared to groan and struggle to breathe. He had to be electrocuted again before he finally died, but not after a two-minute wait, while a Westinghouse AC dynamo recharged. His second electrocution lasted between one and two minutes. The officers, physicians and witnesses were too ill from the horror of the execution to keep the time. The pungent odor of burning flesh and the accompanying crackling sounds haunted those present. Some threw up and one fainted. Almost all sobbed or were tear-eyed. A witnessing *New York Times* reporter claimed that it was "an awful spectacle, far worse than a hanging." George Westinghouse, who did not want his product used to kill, commented: "They would have done better using an axe."

In the case of William Taylor's execution in 1893 at the Auburn Prison, his convulsions were so strong that his leg bones broke during the repeated convulsions, and he had to be removed from *The Chair* and given morphine for the pain and chloroform to render him unconscious, only to return him to the death chair to be electrocuted some more.

There have also been instances of the human skin sticking to *The Chair*. These occurrences, plus the release of bodily fluids during the electrocution, require that *The Chair* be thoroughly scrubbed before the next use.

Part VI. For Pontón

"¡No me dejen solo! ¡No me dejen solo!" ("Don't leave me alone!")
- Antonio Pontón, in his letter to the People of Puerto Rico,
November 1915

~

"Dear Governor Whitman, ..."
"Our father is not a simple criminal. ..."
"He was harassed by more ideas than his mind could stand. ..."
"There is a strain of insanity in his collateral family. ... If the jury knew
of these facts, the verdict would have been different. ..."
"This is the first petition of its kind the island of Puerto Rico. ..."
"He is the son of one of the best good standing families in our
island. ..."
"[He is] the first Porto Rican ever executed by the United States
Government in any of the States of the Union. ..."
"... the horror under which the death penalty is regarded in this
country ..."
"He killed, not knowing how or when. ..."
"Our fellow student is not a criminal. ..."
"We are all united, from the rich planter to the poor worker,
desperately begging you ..."
"... thousands of signatures begging for mercy ..."
"Our entire island, begging for his sentence to be commuted. ..."
"He was insane ... and is insane now ... commutation is the most
advisable thing to do. ..."
"On Thanksgiving Day, during our family gathering, we pray you to
have mercy on Antonio Pontón."

- Excerpts from hundreds of letters and telegrams addressed to
Governor Whitman from Puerto Ricans, November-December 1915

Chapter 51. Motion for a New Trial and Appeal of Murder Verdict

On April 27, 1915, Homer J. Borst, Antonio's defense attorney, served a *Notice of Appeal* and *Motion for New Trial* on District Attorney A. T. Blessing, appealing Antonio Pontón's murder verdict and requesting a new trial. The grounds for the appeal and motion presented the exceptions taken during the murder trial, which included the violations of the defendant's constitutional rights and the newly discovered evidence of insanity, yet to arrive from Puerto Rico. The appeal acted as a stay of the judgment until the Court of Appeals took action.

The attorneys argued the motion on September 4, 1915. Defense attorney Nellis alleged that Antonio had not had a fair trial, among other reasons, because the Lunacy Commission's findings had not arrived from San Juan in time for trial with the family history supporting the insanity defense.

Attorney Frank Antonsanti led the commission's investigation in San Juan to collect the evidence of insanity for Antonio's murder trial, but the information arrived after the murder verdict was entered, and the jury did not have an opportunity to consider it. This report was now in the hands of the defense attorneys.

The newly discovered evidence consisted of affidavits and other documents gathered in large part through the efforts of Reverend Andrés Echevarría, Pastor of *La Iglesia de Nuestra Señora de la Asunción* (Our Lady of the Asuncion Church) in Cayey Puerto Rico, and Sixto Pontón, Antonio's brother.

The documents presented included a family tree containing up to 69 names of members of the Pontón family and extending back for several generations. The names of insane family members were marked in red and those who were sane in white. The red names greatly outnumbered the white. A total of 34 names were for individuals who were deemed insane or with an unsound mind. There were affidavits declaring that two aunts of Antonio were insane, and other affidavits from physicians who attended Antonio and who certified to his insanity during his early life before he went to study at Albany Law School. There were additional documents certifying to the insanity of several other members of the family. The documents were sealed with the great seal of Puerto Rico, described as a massive affair of gold and ribbons, nearly as large as some of the papers to which it was affixed. There was also a $1 revenue stamp on each paper.

The Appeal was scheduled for hearing with Justice Edward C. Whitmyer, who referred it to Justice Van Kirk. After the hearing, Van Kirk denied the motion for a new trial, and the appeal moved to the Court of Appeals, the highest court in New York.

. . .

Antonio's attorneys argued the appeal on October 18, 1915. They based their argument on various points, one being that Antonio's medical examination in the jail by Dr. Scott and Dr. Pashayan was illegal because Antonio's counsel was not present, and Antonio was not informed that the evidence gathered by the doctors would be used against him on his murder trial. Also, Dr. Kellert testified for the defense that Antonio's blood showed he was "far advanced in a state of mental degeneration," and Dr. Charles L. Bailey of Albany testified that Antonio was "suffering from a mental disorder arising from an acquired disease" and his insanity was not limited to his family history.

On October 29, 1915, the Court of Appeals evaluated the evidence, and it did not find that the alleged constitutional violations and the medical evidence of insanity presented by the defense was sufficient justification for a reversal. The court denied the appeal and affirmed the lower court's conviction, with no opinion. Justices Willard Bartlett, Frank Harris Hiscock, Frederick Collin, John W. Hogan, Benjamin Cardozo, Samuel Seabury and Cuthbert W. Pound all concurred.

On October 29, 1915, the front page of the *Albany Evening Journal* read: "Court of Appeals Next Week Will Fix Date for Electrocution of Porto Rican Who Killed Bessie Kromer."

. . .

Many of the Court of Appeals judges who affirmed Antonio's case are considered luminaries today. The fact that they did not even render an opinion regarding the evidence of insanity is disturbing, but the biases of the times, personal and societal, weighed on their decision. Many of the judges had political aspirations, such as Judge Seabury, who ran for governor of New York and lost. Judge Cardozo moved on to become a United States Supreme Court Justice in 1932, and Judge Pound was nominated but was not selected. And then there was Judge Frank Harris Hiscock, who had a personal experience with the murder of his own father, who passed away when the judge was only 11 years old.

In 1867, General George W. Cole shot Luther Harris Hiscock, a Syracuse lawyer, at a renowned hotel in Albany. When the General fired at close range, he stated that Hiscock "violated my wife while I was at the war; the evidence is clear, I have the proof." Both families were rather prominent, and the matter drew much press coverage. The first trial resulted in a hung jury, and the second trial acquitted the general "by reason of momentary insanity." The jury did not find premeditation, although from the killer's statements the murder seemed quite deliberate. Only the judge knew if the desire to avenge his father's murderer weighed in on his court decisions.

Everyone carries their burden along wherever they go.

Judges are not infallible.

Chapter 52. The Voice of a Man Condemned to Die

Antonio Pontón's execution was now scheduled for the week of December 20, 1915. The only hope left was to persuade Governor Charles S. Whitman to issue clemency and commute the court's death sentence. This would be no easy task, as Whitman had proven to be unyielding on crime and clemency, and he was reluctant to interfere with the courts.

Born in Connecticut in 1868, Governor Charles Seymour Whitman studied law at New York University and was admitted to the bar in 1894. In 1909 he was elected New York County District Attorney. He gained fame when he prosecuted New York City Police Lieutenant Charles Becker for the murder of gambler Herman Rosenthal in 1912. He also prosecuted Father Hans B. Schmidt for the murder of his pregnant lover Anna Müller. Whitman served as the 41st Governor of New York from January 1915 to December 1918. During Antonio's ordeal, Whitman was preparing to run for his reelection in 1916, when he would also be elected chairman of the Republican National Convention.

Per his lawyers' recommendation, the first week of November of 1915 Antonio wrote a sincere letter to the major newspapers in Puerto Rico, begging for help in his life-saving plea to the governor. He needed to seize the support of as many souls as possible to draw Whitman's attention to his case.

Antonio's letter was not only unprecedented, but it was also heartfelt and moving. Puerto Rican newspapers, including *La Democracia* and *El Tiempo*, published his plea under the headline *La Voz de un Hombre Condenado a Muerte* (The Voice of a Man Condemned to Die). The letter captured the hearts of every Puerto Rican in the island and abroad, as well as many non-Puerto Ricans who took on the worthy cause.

"With the greatest pain my soul could bear I direct these lines to you," Antonio wrote, requesting from the newspapers the favor of publishing his letter. "The one who writes is the unfortunate Puerto Rican who is now in the Sing Sing Prison in the State of New York, sentenced to die."

Antonio explained that the New York Court of Appeals affirmed his conviction and that without clemency from the Governor of New York, Charles S. Whitman, Antonio would face death on the electric chair.

"I will die like a criminal, when I really am an unfortunate man incapable of containing the thoughts that come to my mind because something inside of me forces me to act," he wrote.

In his letter, Antonio described a life of unhappiness back in Puerto Rico. He said he could not find harmony even with his own family, friends or "the one who was my good wife." He said he failed at everything he attempted. He described how he went to Albany Law School with a great hope to change his fate for the better, and there he met other Puerto Rican students such as Pedro Beiges from Añasco and Vera and López from San Germán, "who are now attorneys." He said the students could attest to his successes and failures at the law school. "Everything was failure for me at the school," Antonio wrote. "They can attest to that fact," he said.

He explained how once in New York he settled in the small town of Schoharie during his first year there to study English. "In this town I met the woman who stole the love in my heart," he wrote. "She seduced me in such a way that I was happy only when I was by her side. Many times I tried to commit suicide because of her," he confessed.

Antonio shared the torment of the distorted thoughts that held his mind hostage, and the impact these had on his behavior. "I cannot explain the thoughts that came to my mind at all times," he said. "To the point that, as you know, I now find myself sentenced to die, awaiting the fatal moment in which my life will be taken away from me the next month of December," he continued his plea.

"Do you think I deserve to die in this country on the electric chair?" Antonio asked. "If you think I am a criminal, let me die, but if you think that I am an unfortunate man, a member of a family disgraced by mental illness," he said, "don't let me die in this country in such a cruel manner." He stated that Father Andrés Echevarría had found that at least 25 members of his family suffered from severe mental illness, suggesting his illness was inherited.

There was no mention in his letter of "the loathsome disease" that had invaded his brain.

Antonio pleaded that his Puerto Rican brothers and sisters form a commission to work with Governor Whitman to commute his sentence, and to help with the legal expenses to represent his history of mental illness, stating that such had not been presented in a proper manner to the jury in his trial. He said that he needed help in bringing these facts to the attention of the Governor of New York. "I am all alone here, and I am begging you to help me pray for clemency from the governor," Antonio wrote.

In his letter, he directed a special appeal to all Puerto Rican women, asking them to think of him as a brother and perform a humanitarian act on his behalf. He stated that their gentle voices are always heard, and asked them to gather signatures and direct the signed petitions to Governor Charles S. Whitman in New York.

"Fight for me," Antonio implored, "my Puerto Rican brothers and sisters." He said that he placed all his hope in them. "If I were guilty, I would not bother you," he assured, stating that he did not deserve to die in such a cruel way, that he was not "a common criminal."

He emphasized the urgency of the matter, as six weeks from the date of his letter he would be executed in the electric chair at Sing Sing. "I wish that a Commission be organized to join Father Andrés Echevarría and Luis Muñoz Rivera, [Puerto Rico's Commissioner] Resident in Washington [D.C.], in the fight to commute my sentence," Antonio wrote. He stated that he knew that his family would be there to support him, in particular his brother Sixto.

Antonio closed his plea to the Puerto Rican people by stating, "You are my only hope." Before sealing the document with his signature, with great desperation, he begged to his compatriots not to abandon him.

"¡No me dejen solo! ¡No me dejen solo!" he said. Don't leave me alone!

His horror and anguish were evident.

Chapter 53. Por Pontón

Antonio Pontón's cry for help touched every Puerto Rican who read his letter. The entire island rose to meet his desperate call. His prayer cut across all social classes, races and ages. All Puerto Ricans united in an unprecedented act to help save their disgraced compatriot.

Time was of the essence. All mayors convened their town councils to discuss their respective responses to Antonio's letter, and they emitted corresponding written resolutions and edicts detailing their course of action to help his case. Dozens of civic organizations arranged meetings and scheduled events to raise money in support Antonio's legal defense fund, and to help mitigate the travel expenses of the commission led by Father Andrés Echevarría, soon heading to New York to persuade Governor Whitman.

"Even if Pontón were not our compatriot, as a neighbor worthy of consideration, he has the right to invoke our love and Christian compassion in the saddest of circumstances of his troubled life," wrote Luis R. Velázquez to the President of the *Casino de Ponce*, a civic organization, enclosing a copy of Antonio's letter and calling for action in support of his cause. "He asks for our humanitarian and noble gratitude" to "mitigate his sorrows however we can ... in favor of a lost compatriot, who finds himself alone, completely alone, in a foreign land," Velázquez urged in his request for a compassionate response.

In the town of *Vega Baja*, a group of ladies passed out invitations to a charitable function to be held at the *Fénix* theatre for the benefit of Antonio Pontón. Luciano Cano, a local musician, was the event organizer, and local artists volunteered their talents. Lola de Portela, President of the *Asociación de Damas,* and women association members volunteered at the box office with much diligence selling tickets for a token donation.

During the month of November of 1915 dozens of articles, letters and notices appeared in the local press across the island with headlines showing solidarity: *"Por Antonio Pontón," "Por Pontón," "En favor de Pontón."* The articles called for the readers' support of their Puerto Rican brother, announced fundraisers, published letters addressed to Governor Whitman, and reported the success of collections undertaken in favor of Antonio's cause.

The *Club Ciencia y Libertad Moral* of the town of *Fajardo* announced a collection. The *Socios del Casino de Cataño* announced a meeting at the local theatre, *Teatro Espinosa*. The *Asociación de Periodistas de Puerto Rico*, journalists in the town of *Arecibo*, would be meeting "for the cause of Pontón."

In *Aguadilla*, a gathering at the residence of González Mena Reichard was announced to convene volunteers "for Pontón." Julio Osvaldo Abril and Francisco de Cardona would lend their automobiles for the purpose of a door-to-door collection in every street in town.

A sympathetic reader from *Vega Baja* wrote a compassionate editorial:

"Antonio Pontón is in the Sing Sing Prison thinking about his island, his beloved mother, the green of our mountains, and the blue sky of his beautiful land. Along with the visions of his tormented soul, he thinks about the fact that his eyes will never see these beauties again; never the perfumed winds of *Borinquen* will caress his face, where misfortune has left its mark, the black seal of his defaming crime! ... Oh! Antonio Pontón, disgraced compatriot! If there is Providence and our prayers reach the heavens, the sound waves emitted from the gentle *Borinquen* will travel across the ocean embraced by our perfumed wind to caress your face, to sooth your soul, and even there in the depths of prison you will feel the love sent by your people, who cry this sweet, noble and loving word: Forgiveness!"

Avid followers of *The Golden Rule*, Puerto Ricans opposed the death penalty, in particular as it applied to the case of an insane man considered irresponsible of his actions. Rich and poor alike, school children and their teachers, men and women, officials, doctors, lawyers, *industriales*, farmers and their workers, all aligned their hearts, prayers and actions to help save the life of the unfortunate Antonio Pontón, who in a bout of insanity, far away from home, committed one of the worst offenses known to man.

They despised his offense, but he deserved their compassion.

Chapter 54. An Entire Island Begs for Clemency

O
n Governor Whitman's desk rested an envelope that arrived the first week of December of 1915, containing a postcard and the photograph of two children of about six and eight years old. The children wrote from Puerto Rico to plead the governor's mercy to spare the life of their father, Antonio Pontón.

"We, Honorable Governor, respectfully appeal to your generosity to beg you to hear the compliments of these two children born of said Pontón actually begging God and you for their father's life. ..." read the children's letter. "Our father is not a simple criminal, but a man of noble heart; and only a victim of a horrible disgrace ... You have been surely a good son and know how sorrow[ful] it will be to see a father in the electric chair," they begged.

The children, Antonio and Manolo, stated that they sent their photograph, as they were unable to travel to Albany in person to "kneel down before you and beg for your generosity for our good father."

Little Antonio and Manolo's letter was one of thousands of pleas received at Governor Charles S. Whitman's office. United States and Puerto Rico government officials, United States Congressmen, university presidents and students, school children and their teachers, community and civic organizations, and individuals from both Puerto Rico and the United States wrote to Whitman in efforts to spare Antonio Pontón's life, appealing to the governor's humanity, faith and compassion, and calling attention to the evidence of insanity that did not make it to trial.

Public officers in Puerto Rico and the United States, such as Arthur Yager (Governor of Puerto Rico), Luis Muñoz Rivera (Puerto Rico's Delegate to Congress and Resident Commissioner), the mayors of the municipalities of Puerto Rico, Martin G. Brumbaugh (Governor of Pennsylvania and former Commissioner of Education in Puerto

Rico), Thomas P. Gore (Chairman of the United States Senate), and James S. Davenport (Chairman of the House of Representatives Committee on the Territories), all sent their urgent appeals by letter and telegram. The country of Spain, through its Spanish Consulate in Washington, D.C. joined the pleas.

Good-hearted Martin G. Brumbaugh, Governor of Pennsylvania, wrote to Whitman: "A dozen or so years ago I was Commissioner of Education in Porto Rico, and learned to know the people there and cherish them with the warmest regard." He enclosed a letter by university students containing arguments supporting their request for clemency.

Chairman of the Senate Thomas P. Gore, Senator for Oklahoma, asked of Whitman, "Permit me to urge that the sentence of death now pending against Antonio Ponton, a native of Porto Rico, be commuted to life imprisonment. ... The fact that there have been several cases of insanity in his family would amply justify such action upon your part."

Representative James S. Davenport, 1st Oklahoma District, said in his letter to Whitman, "I do not appeal for pardon, but at this time I do appeal for a commutation of sentence ... believing that the ends of justice will be finally satisfied by such action if your Excellency, upon an investigation, should believe the circumstances of the case would warrant commutation of the sentence of this unfortunate young man." He closed, "Assuring you of my earnest desire to see Executive clemency extended."

. . .

Back in Puerto Rico, throughout the months of November and December of 1915, town mayors joined the voices of their people by issuing their own official edicts, letters and telegrams addressed to Governor Whitman, some of them sending more than one communication, praying for clemency for Antonio Pontón.

All the municipalities comprising the entire island of Puerto Rico participated, either through their mayors, civic and religious groups, or through individuals: Adjuntas, Aguada, Aguadilla, Aguas Buenas, Aibonito, Añasco, Arecibo, Arroyo, Barceloneta, Barranquitas, Bayamón, Cabo Rojo, Caguas, Camuy, Canóvanas, Carolina, Cataño, Cayey, Ceiba, Ciales, Cidra, Coamo, Comerío, Corozal, Culebra, Dorado, Fajardo, Florida, Guánica, Guayama, Guayanilla, Guaynabo,

Gurabo, Hatillo, Hormigueros, Humacao, Isabela, Jayuya, Juana Díaz, Juncos, Lajas, Lares, Las Marías, Las Piedras, Loíza, Luquillo, Manatí, Maricao, Maunabo, Mayagüez, Moca, Morovis, Naguabo, Naranjito, Orocovis, Patillas, Peñuelas, Ponce, Quebradillas, Rincón, Río Grande, Sabana Grande, Salinas, San Germán, San Juan, San Lorenzo, San Sebastián, Santa Isabel, Toa Alta, Toa Baja, Trujillo Alto, Utuado, Vega Alta, Vega Baja, Vieques, Villalba, Yabucoa, and Yauco. Some of the towns, like Villalba and Cataño, had not been formally established by 1915, but still conveyed their pleas.

The town of *Barranquitas* wrote: "We condemn the crime and honor the memory of the victim. ... At the same time love for our neighbor and compatriot moves us to solicit you reconsider the terrible sentence, modify its extreme rigor and reduce it to life term."

The town of *Santa Isabel* wrote: "Our country is kneeling down before you to ask for forgiveness."

The town of *Juncos* pleaded: "Your brothers under God and under natural law from this part of the universe, loyal to your flag and admirers of your glory, respectfully beg that you extend the hand of clemency to Antonio Pontón, a disgraced man who God knows acted under the influence of a perturbed mind."

A cablegram from the town of *Comerío*, Antonio's hometown, assured the governor that if he granted clemency, "Comerío will remember your condolence forever."

San Juan appealed, stating that General George Washington and President Lincoln were known to not ever deny clemency. "Two qualities heighten mankind, the proper application of the law and the rendering of compassion," the letter stated.

The town of *Fajardo* explained to the governor that this was "the first petition of its kind the island of Puerto Rico has placed before the courts of the United States!"

The Mayor of *Toa Alta* pleaded, "Mercy, mercy for a disgraced man!"

"Avoid the blemish on this poor family that is devastated," wrote the people of *Vieques*, noting the insanity history in Antonio and his family.

The town of *Lajas* urged the governor: "Follow the doctrines of modern criminology and do not execute a demented man."

Statements of faith, morale and reason abounded across the writings sent to the leader of New York. The people of *Trujillo Alto* used maxims to support their plea: "Man has not created life and should not destroy it," "The goodness of men is measured by how they treat bad men," "Jesus said, Father, forgive them, for they do not know what they are doing," "God, the giver of life, is the only one who can take a life."

. . .

An impressive number community and religious organizations convened meetings and gathered signatures back in the island, including firemen, women associations, Catholic and Protestant church organizations, teachers associations, student groups, and worker associations, among many others.

The *League of Puerto Rican Workers* wrote, "Save Pontón from the claws of death." The *Federation of American Workers, Puerto Rico Chapter* said, "We are enemies of the death penalty. ... At the precise moment an inmate is executed, society commits a crime."

The ladies of *San Juan* requested an "act of pity for the first Porto Rican ever executed as a result of a judicial sentence by the United States Government in any of the States of the Union."

The ladies of the town of *Yauco* stated, "If there is no pardon for him, he will die ... in a confining cell ... without kissing the forehead of his mother one last time."

The ladies of the town of *Bayamón* asked for forgiveness for "the son of one of the best good standing families in our island."

A student group named *Eco Estudiantil* from the town of *Río Grande* wrote, "Is it necessary for society to take a life only because one individual has done so? ... Is our society more secure because of our punishing criminals with death? Our study of the history and criminal code in England during the middle ages ... answer[s] ... the above question in the negative."

The *Band of Mercy*, composed of school children from the town of *Ponce,* wrote a lengthy appeal providing numerous reasons for clemency, such as "his history of insanity," "the blot that the execution would throw on the unfortunate and innocent Pontón family, esteemed and regarded in the community ... [and] the horror under which the death penalty is regarded in this country."

The *Centro de Instrucción y Recreo de la Villa de Coamo* (Educational and Recreational Center of the Village of Coamo) wrote,

"Our compatriot is not a vulgar criminal, but a passion-driven man, deserving mercy."

Dozens of additional civic organizations and schools joined in the desperate plea to Governor Whitman, with the hopes that he would be impressed by the vast numbers of people reaching out: *Asociaciones Locales de Maestros* (Teachers Associations) of the towns of *Aguadilla, Yauco, Juncos, Salinas, Ponce, Río Piedras* (a jurisdiction of *San Juan) and Añasco, Bayamón's Disciples of Christ Mission* and its *Christian Women Board of Missions* and *Liga de Temperancia* (Temperance League), *Centro Español de Ponce*, farmers from *Sabana Grande*, firemen from *San Germán* and *Ponce, Sociedad Teosófica Ananda* in Ponce, *Círculo Espiritista de Manatí, Asociación Literaria San Alfonso, Liga Regeneración de Guayama, Liga Literaria Cristiana de Puerto Rico, Liga Progresista de Ponce, Minerva Society, 6th Graders from Añasco* and the *Asociación de Dependientes de Ponce* were among the many civic organizations vested in the cause. Hundreds of signatures supported the pleas.

Puerto Rican Masonic Lodges were highly active in their communications with Governor Whitman. The *Logia Verdaderos Hermanos* from the town of *Coamo* wrote, "He killed, not knowing how or when."

The *Tanamá* Lodge in the town of *Arecibo* said, "We want to state, plainly, that it is not customary for the inhabitants of this island to commit blood crimes as the one perpetrated by our fellow citizen, Mr. Antonio Pontón." The letter explained that Antonio committed the crime under an "irresistible impulse of madness and obsession." The letter stated, "As a typical man of this zone, Mr. Pontón has a tropical temper of romantic imagination and weak to the passion of love." Referring to Antonio's love for Bessie Kromer, the letter said, "He consecrated her as an idol."

La Logia Almas Unidas from the town of *Cidra* wrote, "Those who have been acquainted with him know that he could not have been sane when he committed the crime."

Letters by other Masonic Lodges echoed their Mason brothers' sentiments: *Logia Regeneración No. 110* from the town of *Guayama*; *Logia Luz de Oriente Num. 8.376* from the town of *Yauco, Logia Obreros Unidos* (formed under the *Federación del Grande Oriente Español)* from the *town of Arecibo, Grande Oriente Español* Lodge from the town of *Ponce, Logia Perla del Océano* from the town of

Arroyo, Logia Los Hijos de la Luz from *Yauco* (formed under *Gran Logia Soberana de Puerto Rico), Logia Sol Naciente* from *Aguadilla, Logia Unión 10* from *Guayama, Logia Luz de Borinquen, Caballeros de la Verdad No. 37 and Logia Amparo* from *Caguas; and Logia Fraternidad Española de Ponce,* among others.

Letters with hundreds of signatures from Puerto Rican school children and their teachers poured onto the governor's desk. The *Reina School* students from the town of *Ponce* wrote, "We would like to ask you a favor that if not refused, we will remember you with the most gratitude. The idea that our compatriot will receive the death penalty far away from his parents, brothers and the rest of his family impresses us so."

The teachers and pupils of the town of *Maricao* assured the governor, "Under the strain of a bitter disappointment his mind gave way."

Grade school students from *Río Grande* stated, "Leave his punishment to the one whose power he usurped, and do not stain the name of society with another crime, as terrible as the first."

Among the individuals directly addressing the governor was the entire family of Albany Law School alumnus Ulpiano Crespo, from the town of *Arecibo.* An ex-classmate of Antonio Pontón, Ulpiano Crespo was now a lawyer. "On Thanksgiving Day, during our family gathering, we pray you to have mercy on Antonio Pontón and commute the death penalty, which he is bound to suffer in the near future," stated the letter, signed by Ulpiano Crespo's father, mother and their 15 children.

An anonymous letter signed by *Un Puertorriqueño* ("A Puerto Rican") appealed to the governor by impressing the pain of an entire island. "We are all united, from the rich planter to the poor worker, desperately begging you, do not allow the arrival of the fatal day for this disgraced man," its author wrote. "The Sixth Commandment states 'Thou Shalt Not Kill,'" he wrote, indicating that the mandate also applies to society as a whole, including its leaders.

. . .

Among the hundreds of letters with thousands of signatures begging for clemency for Antonio Pontón, the governor also received letters from university students, including sophomore law students at the University of Puerto Rico Law School, students from the College of

Agricultural and Mechanical Arts in the town of *Mayagüez*, Puerto Rican students at the University of Pennsylvania, University of Syracuse, Loyola University Medical School, The State College of Pennsylvania and Harvard University.

Puerto Rican students attending the *Loyola University Bennett Medical School* affirmed Antonio's history of mental illness, writing that some of them knew Antonio Pontón "from personal observations and experience" back in Puerto Rico attesting that "he has been subject to occasional fits of insanity." *University of Pennsylvania* students appealed to Governor Brumbaugh, asking him to intercede on Antonio's behalf. "Antonio Pontón, of a good family ... has suffered from insanity. This fact was not brought before the court," they said, mentioning the Commission's efforts, support by Puerto Rico's Governor Yager and Archbishop Jones stating, "Everyone is sending letters and helping him in a pecuniary way. Our strong conviction is that our fellow student is not a criminal."

The University's *Phi Chi Delta* fraternity sent a cablegram to Governor Whitman assuring him that Antonio Pontón "came to this country knowing very little of its people and costumes. He suffered a delusion that deprived him of the power of differentiating from right and wrong ... He was harassed by more ideas than his mind could stand."

Students from *The State College of Pennsylvania* wrote that Antonio acted "compelled by passional lunacy" and petitioned that "if God has allowed him to live to this day, kindly grant him that privilege."

"The Porto Ricans at Harvard University believe that the crime was a horrible one and it should be punished, but death penalty would add to, and not detract from, its horrors," the Harvard students wrote. One of the student signatures on the letter was by *Pedro Albizu y Campos* who would later become a Puerto Rican promoter of ideals for the island's independence from the United States.

Pedro Albizu Campos was a mixed-race Puerto Rican student born in 1891 in the town of Ponce. After studying engineering and chemistry at the University of Vermont, he served in the United States Army during World War I as First Lieutenant but felt demeaned by racism and segregation in the United States. After his military service, he enrolled in Harvard University Law School and was scheduled to graduate in 1921 as class valedictorian. He was asked to prepare his speech, but it is said that one of his professors opposed "the embarrassment that a Puerto Rican represented the class as valedictorian." After graduation, Albizu Campos led the *Puerto Rican Nationalist Party* in 1930, becoming a militant towards the island's cause for independence.

In 1932, Albizu Campos unveiled a racist letter Dr. Cornelius P. Rhoads wrote in 1931 to his colleague Fred W. Stewart, confessing to humanitarian crimes the doctor performed against his Puerto Rican patients. "They are beyond doubt the dirtiest, laziest, most degenerate and thievish race of men ever inhabiting this sphere. It makes you sick to inhabit the same island with them. They are even lower than Italians," Dr. Rhoads wrote. "What the island needs is not public health work but a tidal wave or something to totally exterminate the population ... I have done my best to further the process of extermination by killing off eight and transplanting cancer into several more," he confessed.

A laboratory assistant found the letter before it was mailed and circulated it among peers, later providing it to Albizu Campos in 1932. The latter sent copies of the letter to the government, world organizations and the Vatican, alleging that there was a United States plot to exterminate Puerto Ricans.

An inquiry by the Puerto Rico attorney general on the matter yielded no evidence of the alleged homicidal acts by Dr. Rhoads, and the doctor, who had left Puerto Rico, claimed that his letter was a joke. However, the then Governor of Puerto Rico, James R. Beverley, wrote to the Rockefeller Foundation's associate director in 1932 stating that there was a second letter by Rhoads "worst than the first" which had been suppressed and destroyed by the government. This communication, uncovered in 2002 by an investigator, revived the scandalous Dr. Rhoads matter, resulting in the American Association for Cancer Research (AACR) removing Rhoads' name from one of its prestigious awards.

Albizu Campos used Dr. Rhoads' letter to further his nationalism ideals, which he continued to pursue through the promotion of violent acts against the government in Puerto Rico and the United States. These acts resulted in his long-term imprisonment, where he claimed he was being subject to radiation. In 1964, Governor Luis Muñoz Marín pardoned Albizu Campos after he had suffered a stroke in 1956. He died in 1965.

. . .

On December 5, 1915 Dr. José Julio Henna, a Puerto Rican physician and community leader residing in New York, sent a call for a mass meeting to all Spanish-speaking people in the New York area and others interested in Antonio Pontón's cause, to take place at the Ansonia Hotel. The purpose of the meeting was to raise public awareness about Antonio Pontón's case and obtain a commutation of his death sentence. As a result of the meeting called by Henna, a committee of about 200 people was formed, tasked with collecting signatures and submitting a petition to persuade Governor Whitman to commute Antonio's sentence.

Dr. José Julio Henna was born in 1848 in the town of Ponce, a child of an Englishman and a privileged Puerto Rican woman. Henna had become exiled to the United States prior to the Spanish-American War of 1898 because he devised a plan for the independence of Puerto Rico from Spain. He graduated in Medicine from Columbia University in 1872. In 1898, Dr. Henna, along with Roberto H. Todd, communicated with United States President William McKinley and the Senate in efforts to have them consider Puerto Rico in the plans for Cuban intervention. Dr. Henna eventually supported Puerto Rican annexation to the United States and became a known Puerto Rican community advocate in New York.

. . .

The Ladies from the town of *Bayamón* addressed their plea to President Woodrow Wilson in a lengthy letter, drafted by Angelina Balseiro de Feliú. "Many people here think that whatever we do to try to save Antonio Pontón will be in vain, that we will not be heard," the letter read. "This is a terrible thing, Sir! You, as a father, will understand. His parents are devastated. The mother needs medication in order to be able to sleep. This is such a disgrace for the people of Puerto Rico," the letter stated. "Our entire island hopes for his sentence to be commuted ... and our country will be forever grateful," it said. "Thousands of signatures have been collected, begging for mercy ... Sir, don't think about the punishment, think about the suffering of those parents who are dying of sorrow, and of our entire island, begging for his sentence to be commuted," the Bayamón ladies

236

pleaded. Mrs. Balseiro also wrote a personal note in the letter. "I had a dream that I was begging you in person for the life of this disgraced man, and that you listened, moved. I hope my dream becomes a reality and that you hear the prayers of my sisters and I." The letter concluded, "You will be marrying next month. ... We hope you attend to our prayers so that we can have a peaceful Christmas, blessing you and your wife."

The *Women of Puerto Rico* sent another heartfelt appeal to the President's fiancée, Mrs. Edith Galt Bolling (b 1872), the widow of Norman Galt and a direct descendant of the historical Princess Pocahontas. The letter asked for her assistance in their request that the President intercede with Governor Whitman on behalf of Antonio Pontón.

The President and his bride-to-be were preparing for their wedding scheduled for December 18, 1915 and for their honeymoon trip to Hot Springs Virginia thereafter. The newlyweds were scheduled to return to the White House on January 3, 1916.

With the President's schedule consumed by his wedding plans, the European War and the impending World War I conflict, it was not probable that the President and Ms. Galt Bolling had an opportunity to read and respond to the pleas. The attorney general dealt with these requests on behalf of the President, and he forwarded the writings received at the White House to Governor Whitman's office, without taking a position or making a recommendation.

. . .

On December 8, 1915, an *Albany Evening Journal* editorial read, referring to the delegation of leaders arriving in New York from Puerto Rico to meet with Governor Whitman on the matter of Antonio Pontón:

"What may be in the minds of those Porto Ricans who are said to be on their way to this state to ask Governor Whitman to commute the death sentence of Antonio Pontón, can hardly be imagined. ... Pontón's crime was cruel, if not cold-blooded."

The editorial could not find an argument in favor of commuting the death sentence. While there was sorrow for the two young children who would lose their father, their true existence was even questioned. The editorial went as far as suggesting that Antonio's children were impostors.

Among the thousands of clemency letters received by Whitman, there was only one advocating for execution. It was from a man by the name of Jack Hunter, who hand-wrote it on December 9, 1915, expressing similar thoughts to those stated in the editorial.

"Pontón committed one of the most cold-blooded and cruelest deeds. If there is any clemency for his deed, there is no justice in law... Electrocution is too easy a death. If he has children 'which is doubtful' he is a worse villain ... That his electrocution did not take place on July 7 is surprising," he signed, "Respectfully, Jack Hunter."

The Governor received various other letters from American individuals. Among them, there was a letter from Mrs. Anna E. Warner. "Our Dear Governor ... You have the power of life or death for that man. Not his destiny alone is at stake. I pray you to pardon him as heavily as you want the pardon of your heavenly father," she wrote. Mrs. Warner joined many in her belief that a killing is a killing under God, whether committed by a man, or by the governor acting on behalf of society to enforce its terrene laws.

. . .

The Puerto Rican delegation of about 125 individuals, including Reverend Andrés Echevarría, arrived in New York on December 14, 1915 to meet with Governor Whitman. They would ask him to commute Antonio Pontón's death sentence, or in the alternative, grant a respite of 60 to 90 days, such that the new evidence of insanity could be heard. The delegation brought thousands of additional requests from Puerto Ricans pleading for Antonio's life.

Father Echevarría's own written plea enumerated the grounds for clemency in an effort to persuade Whitman. Among the points he made about Antonio were: "1. There is a strain of insanity in his collateral family; 2. The insanity, although collateral, is close to him, as two of his mother's sisters are insane; 3. [Due to the degree of insanity in the different branches of the family] there is a reason to believe that the whole tree is contaminated; 4. It is possible that if the jury knew of these facts, the verdict would have been different; 5. The insanity information was not received from Puerto Rico in time for the trial and the man is not responsible for the negligence of other people; 6. In the opinion of many doctors and other people, the man is insane."

The priest stated to Whitman that the requested clemency "is a courtesy that the people of Puerto Rico would appreciate as a Christmas gift to the island." He also stated that they would appeal to President Woodrow Wilson, if necessary, to have the execution delayed.

. . .

Joining the commission was New York City attorney Charles E. Le Barbier, who after evaluating the case file, including the family tree and other evidence, on December 18, 1915 wrote a persuasive letter to the governor:

"The case seems to present itself to me from an entirely new angle in that there was not submitted to the jury the question of the mental condition of the defendant at the time the act was committed," Le Barbier wrote to Whitman. "I would respectfully refer your Excellency to page 449 of the printed case, Folio 1347, where the learned trial court charged the jury as follows: 'We have had no direct testimony here that this man was in a condition of mind where he did not know the difference between right and wrong.' Le Barbier continued, "Your Excellency will observe, in an important trial such as this one was where under the ordinary plea of 'Not Guilty' it was sought to show that the ... defendant was in a diseased condition, that nevertheless, following it up pathologically, no evidence was presented to the learned trial court nor to the jury as to the mental condition of the defendant ... I respectfully submit that this is a question of fact and indeed a most important fact that should have been presented for the consideration of the jury."

Le Barbier requested from the governor a reprieve to enable the attorney to evaluate the alienists' information and all other information on the issue "in order to prepare a motion before the trial court to show cause and request a new trial."

After the meeting with the Puerto Rico delegation concluded, the press questioned Governor Whitman about Antonio's case. The governor announced to reporters that he was not going to pardon or commute Antonio's sentence, despite the many requests.

But soon after, Whitman changed his mind.

Chapter 55. The Respites

On December 21, 1915, the week of Antonio Pontón's scheduled electrocution, Governor Whitman granted a two-week respite, although he had previously declined to interfere with the execution.

The governor gave no reason for his decision. However, Father Echevarría, having a Power of Attorney from Antonio's father Manuel Pontón, had engaged attorneys Charles Le Barbier and his partner A. Joalyn M. Mcgrath of New York City to obtain a court order from the Supreme Court allowing a physical and mental examination of Antonio. Justice Alden Chester granted the order. Judge Chester lectured on *The Federal Judicial System* at Albany Law School when Antonio was enrolled there as a student.

Two renowned physicians, Drs. Edward A. Spitzka and Harold Lyons Hunt, were to examine Antonio under court order. After the medical examination, the defense planned to move again for a new trial before Justice Van Kirk.

Dr. Edward Anthony Spitzka (b 1876), a native of New York City, was recognized as one of the world's leading brain anatomists. He was also a Professor at Columbia University authoring a number of publications, including a number of "Gray's Anatomy" editions. In addition, in 1901 Dr. Spitzka had autopsied the brain of Leon Czolgosz, the assassin of President William McKinley. He was also the son of famous neurologist Edward C. Spitzka, former President of the American Neurological Association, the author of *Treatise on Insanity*, and most saliently, the physician who signaled the electrocution of William Kemmler, the first man executed by electricity.

The second alienist, Dr. Harold Lyons Hunt, was born in Ontario, Canada on 1882, the same year Antonio was born. He was a child prodigy physician who entered medical school when he was 14 years old and excelled across the board in a number of medical fields. He later became one of the most world-renowned plastic surgeons, widely published on the subject. Dr. Hunt entered military service as Captain of the United States Army Medical Corps in 1917 and fought in World War I, being honorably discharged in 1919. A proponent of peace, he filed for a copyright for "Dr. Hunt's World Peace Plan" in 1923, and held a patent for a land mine designed to prevent American soldier war casualties.

On December 30, 1915 after the doctors examined Antonio Pontón, Dr. Spitzka sent a telegram to Governor Whitman communicating the results, in which he stated:

"Pursuant to an order of the Supreme Court to examine the mental and physical condition of Antonio Ponton in conjunction with Dr. Lyons Hunt I did make such examination. I find him profoundly insane that he was so at time act was committed and it has extended down to present time is progressive and incurable. Dr. Hunt and I find him suffering from a chronic delusional insanity not knowing the differences between right and wrong and that it could be a miscarriage of justice if the man was executed. Dr. Edward Anthony, Spitzka, 63 E 91 St."

The next day, Luis Muñoz Rivera, Puerto Rico's Resident Commissioner to Congress, also sent a cablegram to the governor, stating:

"As the representative of Porto Rico in the United States I join my request to that of the Commission composed of Father Echeverria alienists and lawyers who will visit you today in behalf of Pontón I also believe that he was insane at the time of the commission of the crime and is insane today and that a commutation is the most advisable thing to do. L M Rivera Resident Commissioner."

On December 31, 1915 Governor Whitman granted another reprieve to Antonio, who had been scheduled to die on the electric chair at Sing Sing on Monday January 3, 1916. The governor's action was said to be in response to the plea by Antonio's attorneys, supported by assertions of incontrovertible proof of his insanity by the medical opinions of Drs. Edward A. Spitzka and Harold Lyons Hunt. In addition, the governor was in possession of a petition containing 15,000 signatures of Puerto Ricans residing in the United States, submitted by the Committee organized by Dr. J. J. Henna.

Governor Whitman granted a delay in execution until Friday, January 7, 1916 so that Antonio's attorneys could motion to the court with the new evidence.

Chapter 56. From Osborne to New Warden Kirchwey

At the time Antonio arrived in Sing Sing, the prison's warden was Thomas Mott Osborne, a radical prison reformer who had become warden in 1914. Born in 1859 in New York, Osborne graduated from Harvard University with honors in 1884, where he was among the founders of the *Harvard Cooperative Society* (today known as *The Harvard Coop.*) His family included eminent women's rights reformers. He spoke against slavery and served two terms as mayor of Auburn. Osborne spent a week in the Auburn State Prison in 1913 under the name of "Tom Brown," to see for himself what it was like to be a prisoner there. He recorded his experiences in the book *Within Prison Walls,* which he published in 1914, making him the most prominent prison reformer of his day and helping to end prisoner abuses common in United States prisons at the time.

As Sing Sing Warden, Osborne established a system of prisoner self-rule called *The Mutual Welfare League*, and it was not long before he won enthusiastic support from both guards and most prisoners. In fact, the day of Antonio Pontón's arrival to Sing Sing coincided with the delivery of the *New York Yankees* baseball team's old uniforms, part of Osborne's initiative to improve the morale of the mainstream inmates by forming a Sing Sing prisoner baseball team.

Although Osborne's initiatives were well-received by many, high-profile and wealthy prisoners who manipulated the prison system by intimidating inmates and bribing guards, were not at all pleased with Osborne's tipping of the balance at the prison. In early January of 1916, while Antonio was a prisoner in Sing Sing, these high-profile prisoners used their influence to force Osborne to take a leave of absence, while being tried for false allegations they planted against him.

Osborne later triumphed in court and his return to Sing Sing later

243

in 1916 was much celebrated. However, he would resign at the end of 1916, leaving a tangible legacy of prison reform, but tired of battling his superiors and Governor Charles S. Whitman.

. . .

Before going on leave, Osborne sent Governor Whitman a telegram confirming the December 20, 1915 respite for Antonio Pontón, which had postponed his execution to January 3, 1916. Osborne's friend and colleague, George W. Kirchwey replaced him. New Warden Kirchwey's first day in Sing Sing was scheduled for January 4, 1916.

Born in Michigan in 1855, Kirchwey was a lawyer, politician, journalist and legal scholar. A Yale College graduate, former Dean and Professor of both, Albany Law School and Columbia Law School, Kirchwey was a pioneer in the introduction of the Case Method of studying law. He was also an avid advocate of prison reform, eventually becoming a commissioner on prison reform for the state of New York. He also became the president of *The American Peace Society* in 1917.

The first act in Kirchwey's new official capacity as prison warden was to file the warrant granting a reprieve to Antonio Pontón until January 7, 1916. In his first day of work, Warden Kirchwey made it clear to the press that he was no friend of the death penalty, let alone of electrocuting a fellow human being. When a reporter from the *New York Sun* asked him if he would be present if Antonio Pontón were electrocuted, Kirchwey replied, "I find that the law permits a warden if sick or disabled to absent himself [from the execution of a man.] You may rest assured that I will be sick or disabled at that time. If I had my choice I rather a man had to electrocute me than I to electrocute him."

Chapter 57. The Last Motion

Antonio Pontón's new attorney, Charles E. Le Barbier, the prominent New York City lawyer and former New York District Attorney, went before Justice Charles C. Van Kirk to motion for a new trial with the new evidence containing the findings of alienists Drs. Hunt and Spitzka.

When the *New York Herald* interviewed Hunt and Spitzka about their findings, Dr. Hunt shared the doctors' opinion, consistent with what they had relayed to Governor Whitman.

"There can he no doubt but Ponton is insane and that his legal execution would be a miscarriage of Justice," Dr. Spitzka said to the reporter. "The proof of his mental irresponsibility I believe is absolute. He is suffering now from chronic delusional insanity and was suffering in the same manner at the time he committed the crime," he continued. "Even now, Ponton does not realize that Ms. Kromer is dead and in his cell in the Sing Sing *Death House* constantly calls for her and refers to her as the sweetheart with whom he will be reunited," Spitzka said. "Many ... tests which we have made convince us that he should not suffer the death penalty, but that he should be transferred to a hospital for the criminally insane," he concluded, resolute.

The doctor reiterated that at least 13 of Antonio's relatives had been adjudged absolutely insane. He also stated that the doctors learned that back in Puerto Rico, "Antonio Pontón drove a horse off the edge of a high cliff just to see what would happen to the animal, and on another occasion he drove an automobile with passengers at high speed backward for 20 miles."

The renowned doctors asserted that there was a history of mental illness before, during, and after the commission of the crime. They warned that "executing this man would be a miscarriage of justice."

Still, despite the mountains of evidence of insanity and the qualified expert medical testimony by a total of four renowned and qualified expert witnesses, the court denied the last motion.

Antonio Pontón would be executed on Friday, January 7, 1916.

Part VII. In the Shadow of Death

"I appeal to your sentiments of humanity in behalf of Ponton after the alienists opinion being expressed I believe you have a sufficient ground for commutation."
- *Luis Muñoz Rivera, Puerto Rico's Resident Commissioner to Congress, Washington, D.C.*
Telegram to Governor Whitman, January 6, 1916

"In view of the judgment of the alienists that the man is insane would it not be possible to commute sentence to life imprisonment I would appreciate such action."
- *Arthur Yager, Governor of Puerto Rico*
Telegram to Governor Whitman, January 6, 1916

"What you are about to witness is a blot upon the civilization of the twentieth century."
- *Sing Sing Deputy Warden Spencer Miller,*
Addressing Antonio Pontón's execution witnesses on January 7, 1916

Chapter 58. The Last Pleas

O n January 6, 1916, the day before Antonio Pontón's scheduled electrocution, a delegation of Puerto Ricans in Washington D.C. enlisted Governor of Puerto Rico Arthur Yager to try to persuade Governor Whitman one last time. Governor Yager (b 1858) an economist from Kentucky, President Wilson's former classmate and friend, and once President of Georgetown College, tried to persuade Whitman. Puerto Rico's Resident Commissioner in Congress, Luis Muñoz Rivera wrote to Whitman once again. In separate telegrams, both officers appealed to Governor Whitman to spare Antonio's life on grounds that he was "hopelessly insane and was so at the time the crime was committed." In addition, Puerto Rican leader Antonio Vélez Alvarado, and even the Sing Sing Deputy Warden Spencer Miller acting on behalf of Warden Kirchwey, joined the last minute desperate pleas to the unyielding governor.

Governor Yager's January 6th telegram read:

"The people of Porto Rico are profoundly exercised over the impending execution of Ponton tomorrow in view of the judgment of the alienists that the man is insane would it not be possible to commute sentence to life imprisonment I would appreciate such action if it could be made to accord with your judgment and conscience. Arthur Yager Governor of Porto Rico."

Luis Muñoz Rivera's telegram to Whitman on January 6th stated:

"I appeal to your sentiments of humanity in behalf of Pontón after the alienists opinion being expressed I believe you have a sufficient ground for commutation if you adopt that course I anticipate for you the profound gratitude of the people of Porto Rico who are deeply interested in this lamentable affair. L M Rivera Resident Commissioner."

Puerto Rican leader Antonio Vélez Alvarado, representing Dr. J. J. Henna's committee, also joined Yager and Muñoz Rivera's last minute petitions via telegram, saying:

"Inasmuch as the alienists have reported that Antonio Ponton was insane at and before the time of the commission of the crime and that he is now profoundly demented, this petition is respectfully presented requesting that you immediately appoint a commission to examine him as to his sanity. A. Velez Alvarado, Representing the Porto Rican Committee."

Antonio Vélez Alvarado was born in Manatí, Puerto Rico in 1864 and is known as "the Father of the Puerto Rican Flag." He was a Puerto Rican journalist, politician and revolutionary who advocated for Puerto Rican independence. He was also a Freemason and a close friend of Cuban independence patriot José Martí. Vélez Alvarado's parents were the wealthy owners of various farms in Puerto Rico and his father, a former Spanish militia captain in Puerto Rico, had dreams for a military career for his son in Toledo, Spain. However, Vélez Alvarado became a writer and advocated pro-independence from Spain, instead. He was exiled from Puerto Rico, established himself in New York and ran various newspapers. He was also a friend of Dr. José Julio Henna (who had worked so diligently collecting signatures to have Antonio's sentence commuted), even though Vélez Alvarado and Henna espoused opposing views regarding Puerto Rican independence vs. annexation to the United States.

Deputy Warden Miller also addressed Whitman via telegram on January 6th on behalf of Warden Kirchwey, hoping for a last minute status change on Antonio's execution. Miller's telegram stated:

"Would you kindly confer with Warden Kirchwey who is in Albany today reference to Lunacy Commission in Ponton's case wire decision. S Miller Jr."

All pleas were again unsuccessful.

Governor Whitman called the prison the night of January 6th and instructed Assistant Warden Spencer Miller, "Antonio Pontón's execution must go on."

Chapter 59. The Last Mile

Antonio Pontón's execution at Sing Sing was scheduled for 5:45 the morning of Friday, January 7, 1916. Executions were held on Thursdays, but the last respite placed Antonio's on a Friday, instead.

The day before his imminent death, Antonio was restless, but he later calmed down with the help of Father Andrés Echevarría, the good Puerto Rican priest and family friend, who remained in New York.

Antonio held tight to the rosary his mother had sent him.

"What to do now, Father? I am going to die like a killer, and I do not even remember killing."

"You can pray, my son. You are in the hands of God now," said the good priest.

"Will God forgive me?" asked Antonio.

"If you are contrite, Mr. Pontón, God will forgive," said the priest.

Earlier that day, Warden George W. Kirchwey held a press conference to announce that he had made a new rule: "There will be no press in the execution room." Kirchwey made it clear he did not want people "making a spectacle of the death of a fellow man."

Dr. Amos O. Squire, Chief Prison Physician and death penalty opponent, also visited Antonio late afternoon for a last check before the dreaded next morning.

. . .

There was not much sleep that night, especially for Antonio. In and out of his troubled mind, his thoughts haunted him terribly. The events that brought him to Sing Sing, however scrambled in his ill mind. Bessie. The pain and shame he caused his family and compatriots. The impact of his execution on his parents. His young children. The efforts of the Puerto Rican people and other supporters of his cause.

Antonio recalled the torturous sounds of the electrocutions of other condemned men who went before him. The smell of charred flesh and the sound of the screeching saw in the autopsy room, so close to the cells of those still living, floating through the air and into the minds of all *Death House* inmates awaiting the same fate.

Not too far away from Antonio's cell, his fellow death row prisoner, Charles H. Stielow, lay down on his cell cot, all night awake, praying for Antonio and for himself. The innocent man's execution was scheduled not too long after Antonio's, on April 14th.

. . .

As the early sunrays began to cut through the darkness of the *Death House*, the prison keepers appeared in silence to draw the heavy green curtains before the cells, in order to block the view of the fatal procession from the sight of the rest of the inmates. The shrieking sound of the curtain hoops sliding down the metal rods awoke everyone. Some of the prisoners began praying, yet others would also curse in anger and frustration, feeling powerless and forsaken, in empathy with Antonio and dreading their own nearing fate.

"It is time to get ready, Mr. Pontón." An officer removed Antonio from his cell.

"Jessir," Antonio was shaking.

He was bathed, shaven and barbered. The barber shaved the spot on his skull where an electrode would later be attached. Officer Meserole, on duty that morning, escorted Antonio to the pre-execution cell, the *Dance Hall*. Father Andrés Echevarría, who had fought so hard to save Antonio's life, waited inside the cell for him. He sat by Antonio's side praying and bearing the heavy burden of representing Antonio's parents and loved ones from Comerío.

Antonio could not remain seated. He stood up and began pacing back and forth, holding on to the rosary, his pacing matching the rhythm of his heartbeat.

He danced to the waltz of fear and death.

Suddenly, an officer opened the cell gate to let a man inside. It was Vélez Alvarado, who had requested permission to accompany

Antonio during his last moments.

"Mr. Pontón, my name is Antonio Vélez Alvarado. I am here to let you know that your brothers and sisters from Puerto Rico have not abandoned you," he said. "*Usted no está solo.* You are not alone. I am here to represent your compatriots in this trying time."

"*Gracias.* Thank you," said Antonio as he shook the man's hand.

Antonio sat down for a few moments holding on to his rosary as he continued praying with Father Echevarría, shaking his right leg in a nervous sway. The prison Chaplain, Father William E. Cashin, soon joined the men in preparation for the procession of death.

No one expected a reprieve. No one but Antonio.

The sound of keys announced the dreadful moment as the guard opened the cell door. "It is time for the walk, Mr. Pontón," said the officer.

Antonio stood up and began walking. The priests and the compatriot followed him.

Executions at Sing Sing typically proceeded with a ceremonial precision, mostly to avoid disturbance or anything that increased the horror of the occasion, but this did not happen the morning of Antonio's execution.

George Meserole saw another officer suddenly thrust Antonio back into his cell in a hurry and slam the door on his face. Antonio's walk halted, along with all the prayers.

Antonio was terrified.

"Could this mean a reprieve?" Antonio asked, scanning all present with eyes wide-open.

He remembered about others' last minute reprieves, sometimes arriving moments before the switch was drawn.

Antonio could hear his heart pounding. He could feel his hands sweating.

Word in the corridor that a prisoner had escaped trumped the officer's silence. Joseph Hill managed to flee the prison while on an errand and was on top of the roof, guards in hot pursuit of him.

Antonio's fleeting hope was crushed, and the pain of his wait extended.

. . .

The execution's witnesses waited while treated with coffee at the warden's quarters, which remained decorated with Christmas ornaments and a tree. The witnesses for the State were: Warren S. Hastings, an Albany Coroner's office physician, Dr. E. H. Jackson, the Schenectady Coroner who took charge of the murder case, Schenectady Sheriff Louis A. Welch, who took such good care of Antonio while at Schenectady Jail, and Sergeant Charles F. Engel, of the Schenectady Police force, who witnessed the murder and arrested Antonio.

After about half an hour had passed, prison officers apprehended the escaped prisoner. Around 6:00 a.m. the assistant warden asked the witnesses to return to the *White Room*.

. . .

Warden Kirchwey was not at the prison, as he was a firm opponent of capital punishment, much like his predecessor warden Thomas Mott Osborne. Kirchwey left Assistant Warden Spencer Miller and Principal Keeper Fred Dorner to supervise the execution.

In the *White Room*, assistant Warden Miller was indisposed and doubted his self-control during Antonio's electrocution. This particular execution was affecting him more than any other.

"Mr. Dorner," he said to the Principal Keeper. "I have to excuse myself from Mr. Pontón's execution. I am afraid I cannot take the injustice. The man is insane. This is not a lawful execution, in my view. This is murder. I do not wish to distract anyone. I mean, if I were to ... I do not feel well. Can you stand on my behalf?"

"Certainly, Mr. Miller," said Dorner. "This is a difficult time for all. I will stand on your behalf. And I will be there by him."

"Thank you," said Miller. "I apologize, but I just cannot participate. I will make a statement before I step out."

Before excusing himself, Miller spoke to the witnesses in the execution room:

"What you are about to witness is a blot upon the civilization of the twentieth century. I know that you are not here but of morbid curiosity or in a search for sensationalism, and I hope after you will see that, you will do what you can to bring about the abolition of capital punishment so that every man may have a second chance, the ideal to which the new Sing Sing is dedicated."

The witnesses were silent.

"I will excuse myself from the room during the execution. Principal Keeper Dorner will assume supervisory duties," said Miller, right before he left the *White Room*, visibly upset.

As Miller exited, he held the door open for John Hulbert, the executioner, who entered the *White Room* and immediately went into the small room in the back of the death chamber, behind *The Chair*, and closed the door. Like Miller, Hulbert was sick that morning. He was anxious, nauseated and had the chills. Suddenly, he lost his balance and fainted. All men in the *White Room* could hear the thud of his body when it hit the ground, although they were unable to see him.

Dorner rushed to open the door to the small room. He saw Hulbert laying flat on the floor, unconscious.

"Dr. Squire, the electrician has collapsed!" said Dorner. Dr. Squire, Sing Sing Chief Physician, and Dr. H. E. Mereness, Assistant Physician, hurried into the little room.

Hulbert, a short and stocky introverted man, had performed in many executions before, displaying perfect nerves and an excellent constitution, but something was different the morning of Antonio's execution. The executioner avoided reading about crimes in the newspapers, as he did not want to become familiar with a person he later had to execute. He wanted to be totally free from knowledge of the condemned. Perhaps he did not do this with Antonio Pontón. No one knew. Maybe the job had taken an irreversible toll. Dr. Squire observed the latter was probably the case.

"The job has probably caught up to him," Dr. Squire commented.

Fearing that he would not be able to work the electric switch that morning, Dr. Squire and Dr. Mereness gave Hulbert a stimulant to bring him back to consciousness.

"How are you feeling now, Mr. Hulbert?" asked Dr. Squire.

"I feel better, thank you," responded Hulbert, still lightheaded.

"Do you feel well enough to proceed with today's job?" asked the doctor.

"I believe so," answered the executioner, biting his lower lip.

The doctors waited a couple of minutes to monitor the electrician, in case he were to lose consciousness again. Hulbert regained his nerve and prepared to do his job. Everyone left the back room. Principal Keeper Dorner stated that the execution would move forward.

. . .

From his cell, Charles Stielow could hear officers notifying Antonio around 6:10 a.m. that it was time to restart his death walk. He heard a swaying man fall against the wall of his cell and the sobs and entreaties of the murderer, followed by the drone of the chaplains. Then, through a rift in the green curtain, Stielow saw Antonio walk towards the *Green Door*, which then opened and swallowed him away.

. . .

After entering the death chamber, Antonio walked towards *The Chair* with assistance from Dorner. He silently sat on *The Chair's* fangs, all the while praying, accompanied by the two priests. Vélez Alvarado was allowed to join the other witnesses.

The witnesses gazed at Antonio in silence, following his every move. Antonio locked eyes with Sheriff Welch for a moment, but no words needed to be exchanged. The spectacle was new for some, but others had witnessed the killing of other prisoners before, as their jobs demanded it.

Antonio wore a dark suit. Since Kemmler's botched electrocution, the location of the spine electrode was moved to the leg. Hulbert cut a small slit in the fabric of the right leg of Antonio's pants so that he could fasten the first electrode to his calf.

Antonio made a gesture to Mr. Dorner, who approached him.

"No reprieve, Mr. Dorner?" Antonio whispered to the Principal Keeper.

"No, Mr. Pontón. No reprieve," Dorner responded.

"Farewell, Mr. Dorner," he said. "Please tell my people I love them."

"Godspeed, Mr. Pontón," Dorner replied. "Godspeed."

The cold and wet sponge for the second electrode startled Antonio as the executioner attached it to his skull. A wet sponge would ensure proper skin contact to maximize conductivity during the execution. The leather and wire mesh helmet, strapped around his chin, followed the placement of the tight mask over his eyes. Darkness overcame him.

His body slightly reclined backwards. The fangs sunk further onto Antonio's body when the executioner strapped him, the belts constraining his breathing.

Hulbert then strapped Antonio's arms, but he held onto his rosary with his right hand.

"*Padre nuestro que estás en los Cielos.* Our Father who art in Heaven," Antonio continued praying out loud, clenching to his rosary.

"*¡Ay Diós Mío! ¡Ay Diós Mío!*" ("God my Lord! God my Lord!") Antonio said in a shattered and terrified voice.

His last words.

Antonio could hear the priests' drone.

Dr. Squire signaled Mr. Hulbert to throw the switch.

He did.

. . .

Antonio heard the vibration of the switch when it made contact, along with a buzzing sound, and he instantly felt the current spreading through his then living body. His muscles contracted in pain, flinging him forward and backward. His bones aching and shattering, his head and his calf burning. His ears ringing, his nose dripping blood. The skin on his face and eyelids crisping.

He became motionless.

The current was left to course through Antonio's body for several seconds as the law required.

When Hulbert brought the switch back to its original position, Dr. Squire motioned to Father Echevarría to retrieve the rosary from Antonio's hand. The priest approached him. He noticed that the hand had not released its grip and the rosary's metal crucifix had embedded in his skin. Suddenly, Antonio's hand slightly moved. The reverend looked at Dr. Squire, in horror.

. . .

"He is still living!" Antonio heard the priest say, terrified, in total darkness.

There was chatter in the room. He smelled his own charred flesh. He smelled the metallic scent of his blood. He wanted to break free and run away as fast as he could, but his body would not respond to his brain's commands.

The excruciating pain!

He then felt a freezing object on his chest. It was Dr. Squire's stethoscope, listening for any sign of life. Dr. Mereness also followed to auscultate.

Unable to scream, tears came down Antonio's cheeks and trickled down his face and neck, past the loosened mask. The doctors and some witnesses noticed.

With a tight lip, the doctors looked at each other, nodded and retreated from Antonio's body.

Dr. Squire raised his hand once again, signaling at Hulbert that Antonio was still living. The executioner sent the current through Antonio's body a second time.

But his lungs still breathed.

Antonio felt his faulty heartbeat pounding out of sync, amid the chatter. He gargled as he grasped for air but began to choke in his own vomit, unable to move his head.

The smell of burned flesh and body fluids in the room was unbearable.

For a third time the decimating current streamed trough his body.

This time, a soothing breeze caressed Antonio's face. He had broken free from the fangs. He had walked away from the horror and the pain.

"Forgiveness!" the breeze whispered. "Forgiveness!"

His leg and head smoked where the electrodes had burned through his skin. But his body no longer felt the pain. He no longer felt the terror.

Time of death was pronounced at 6:24 a.m.

. . .

The doctors drew the thin white curtains around him. Hulbert took the helmet and mask off, removed the electrodes, and unstrapped Antonio's lifeless body away from *The Chair's* death bite. The doctors placed the corpse on a squealing cot and rolled it away to the autopsy room, the rosary still clinging to his right hand.

As the officers prepared to escort the witnesses and Father Echevarría back to the Warden's office, Father Cashin returned to the *Death House* to calm the other inmates.

The saw began screeching.

Its whine traveled through the air, along with the smell of Antonio's charred skin, into the cells of those still living.

Chapter 60. Without a Hitch

"**A**ntonio Pontón was executed this morning in accordance with the law. Geo W Kirchwey Warden," stated the telegram sent to Governor Whitman's office at 8:40 a.m.

Assistant Warden Spencer Miller walked out of the prison to brief the press. Before he could speak, he broke down and wept over the fact that he had been forced to direct the killing of a fellow man. Then, after composing himself, he advocated for the dissolution of the death penalty.

"Antonio Pontón's execution was a blot upon the civilization of the twentieth century," Miller said to the press, teary-eyed. "It took three shocks to kill him. Time of death was 6:24 a.m." He did not answer any questions. Without more, Miller turned around and returned to the prison.

"Antonio Ponton's execution went without a hitch. He met his fate far more bravely than the witnesses thought he would," the press reported.

Father Andrés Echevarría had made arrangements to transport Antonio's remains back to Puerto Rico.

· · ·

Upon the sounds of Antonio Pontón's electrocution and autopsy, Charles Stielow, recently moved into cell number nine facing the *Green Door* and next to the execution and autopsy rooms, broke down and threw himself on his cot, shaking. Chills took hold of his entire body as the sounds of the saw played. Meserole, the prison officer, went to see what had happened to him.

"What is wrong, Stielow?" he asked through the bars.

Stielow cried, "Oh God! I can't stand it. Move me to another cell!"

Meserole replied, "You'll get used to it."

Stielow lay there, praying to God, without any clarity about his future, and without assurance that his sentence would be revoked, even though he was an innocent man.

Angelo Leggio, a fellow *Death House* inmate who occupied cell number ten, across from Stielow's and also facing the Green Door, had seen Antonio's death march and felt the sounds and smells, as well. In anguish, he lost all hope that his own life be spared. His own execution was scheduled for the next week, on January 13th.

That evening, Stielow saw Leggio piling books against his cell door, and although he wondered what Leggio might be up to, Stielow was exhausted and fell asleep. At around midnight, the guards made tremendous noises, awaking all men.

Leggio had hung himself.

He had wrapped his bed sheets around his neck, climbed up the book tower he had made, and kicked the books away, falling to his death.

He had cheated justice.

. . .

Executioner Hulbert continued to feel ill that day, and he was taken to the hospital, where he stayed a few days. After his release, he resumed doing his job. He was paid $150 per execution and needed the money to support his wife and three children. Over time, he grew increasingly anxious, was depressed and lost a good amount of weight. He eventually suffered a nervous breakdown and resigned his post.

"I'm tired of killing people," he said to the press the day he resigned.

A couple of years after Hulbert retired, his son found him shot to death in the basement of his home. He had committed suicide.

. . .

News stories about Antonio Pontón quickly dissipated in New York. The press moved on in haste to other fresh news, reporting on the next spectacle.

But it was not over in Comerío.

Part VIII. Home

I AM LEAVING BECAUSE THE EARTH IS NO LONGER MINE
Because my feet are weary,
my eyes blind,
my mouth parched
and my body docile and light,
ready to enter the air.
I am leaving because there are no paths left for me to follow on the
ground.
I emerged from water, I have lived in blood
and now the Wind awaits
to take me to the sun ...
I emerged from the sea ... and I will expire in flames.

- A segment from the poem "Me Voy" ("I am Leaving"),
by León Felipe (Author's Translation)

Chapter 61. La Décima

News about the first Puerto Rican executed on the electric chair quickly traveled throughout Puerto Rico, much like Antonio's letter and the outpour of support by his compatriots and loved ones had, a couple of months earlier. His execution shook not only the people of Comerío, a town that loved the Pontón family and witnessed their son grow up, but it also set the entire island of Puerto Rico into mourning.

Their prayers had not been heard. Antonio Pontón was executed, despite the overwhelming evidence of his mental illness and the loud cries of an entire island.

Trovadores sang the *décima* (a ten line stanza of poetry) *"El Puertorriqueño Ejecutado en Nueva York"* ("The Puerto Rican Executed in the United States") at the mountains, the streets and the *plazas.* It told of Antonio's last letter to his ailing parents and of his execution. Young Antonio, while he was given the free will to guide the dreadful actions that brought about his ultimate fate, was still a human being who suffered, and so did his parents.

I am going to die, my angel
Amidst bitterness and pain
Over my cold tomb
No one will place a flower
Antonio Pontón is already dead
His fate was fulfilled
In the United States
Capital of New York
May God give him strength and valor
May He light his free will
A letter he has directed
Saying farewell to his father

Antonio's Will

And he says to his grief-stricken mother
I am going to die, my angel ...

- *Excerpt from the popular Décima*
"The Puerto Rican Executed in the United States"
(Author's Translation)

~

Voy a morir angel mío
Entre amargura y dolor
Sobre un sepulcro frío
No hay quien me ponga una flor
Ya murió Antonio Pontón
Su signo se le ha cumplido
En los Estados Unidos
Capital de New York
Diós le de fuerza y valor
Le alumbre el libre albedrío
Una carta ha dirigido
Despidiéndose del padre
y le dice a la triste madre
Voy a morir angel mío ...

- *Segmento de la Décima popular*
"El Puertorriqueño Ejecutado en los Estados Unidos"

Chapter 62. Manuel's Dream

W hen it visited, *la musa del sueño* (the sleep muse) comforted Manuel and Etervina's pain. But she did not stop by often.

Dreams placed a veil over the awful face of reality, even if for a fleeting moment. The night of Antonio's execution, the muse brought Manuel a nightmare, soothed by an unusual manifestation of peace.

In Manuel's dream, Antonio's body had arrived in Comerío, all the while guarded by Father Echevarría. To spare Manuel and Etervina any more heartbreak, Antonio's siblings undertook the heavy burden of arranging for their brother's funeral ceremony at the town's church, *Santo Cristo de la Salud* (Holy Christ of Health), followed by his burial in the town's cemetery. Family, friends, officials, and workers were all there.

Father Echevarría led the walking procession joined by the townspeople, escorting Antonio's body and his family from their home to the church and then to his final resting place.

As the Reverend paced through Antonio's second and final procession of death, the last moments of Antonio's life at Sing Sing kept playing in the good priest's mind, like an infinite motion picture. In his head echoed the words of the inmates as their fellow prisoner walked towards the green door: "Goodbye Antonio," "Stay strong now," "See you on the other side," "God bless your soul," "*Adiós,*" "Farewell!"

Antonio's last words pierced the priest's soul, "*¡Ay Diós Mío! ¡Ay Diós Mío!*" uttered as he clenched onto his rosary, the only comfort he had left, clamping to it as a frightened child to his mother.

At the cemetery, Father Echevarría spoke a few words as Antonio's coffin, holding his charred and autopsied corpse, was about to be placed into his tomb. In the background, he could hear the crying sobs of the women, children and of many men, intermingled with the sounds of gusts of wind caressing the leaves of the surrounding *flamboyanes* (jacaranda trees) surprisingly in bloom for that time of the year.

Antonio's children stood by their mother, their gaze fixed on their father's coffin. An image carved in their minds for eternity.

The good priest began to speak.

"It is true that for all of us mortals, death is certain, and we must live while we wait for the veil of death to forever steal our breaths and seal our eyes. But our anticipation is not level with the torturous wait of those facing the doom of an execution.

While we await death, we become distracted by the adventure called life, unaware of the instant when it will set foot on our doorstep. For the most part, unless sickness or old age takes us hostage, we do not delve on this occurrence much.

Those in the so called 'death house' at the Sing Sing Prison in New York live in constant anguish, dreading the arrival of their meeting time with death, counting the days, hours, minutes and seconds until the very moment that will shock and burn the life away from their veins. Still, with every single breath, they wish and pray for a second chance at life.

Where is justice in such a twisted experiment?

It is also true that those who violate the rights of others must face a consequence for their actions. But shouldn't such consequence be compassionate?

Unlike many of us, blessed by God with a healthy mind, those who are inflicted with a mental illness are not afforded the means to tell right from wrong. They have lost their free will. They are like children, regardless of their age.

How can humans condemn an erring man to perish at their hand in such a horrible way? How can they condemn an insane man to death? Who gives them the right to murder?

To be fair, justice must kill!

'An eye for an eye,' the fable of vengeance literally becomes the law, becomes the guiding light of modern society.

The Holy Book says in Mathew 10:28: 'Do not be afraid of those who want to kill your body, as they cannot touch your soul.'

They took Antonio's body, but they could not take his soul. It is now resting peacefully with our Lord, and we shall let it be so.

He went bravely, despite his confused and troubled mind. He could not comprehend the actions for which he was receiving the ultimate punishment. He had to be reminded of the dreadful facts. As he waited for death, he was all the while in prayer; all the while sorrowful for the pain he imposed on his parents, his family and loved ones. He dreaded having caused the death of his victim.

All of us shall always remember that our time will come, too; we just do not know when. So, let us make the best choices we can make at this very moment, and let us live a fruitful and productive life, always.

We must also show compassion for those who are mentally ill, as their minds cannot make the choices that those with a sane mind can make. These creatures of God feel all alone in the world, taunted by the torture of their disfigured thoughts. Let us have mercy on them and their souls.

Let us have mercy on Antonio Pontón. May he rest in peace forever.

Amen."

As the *sepulturero* sealed Antonio's grave with the heavy tombstone, the crowd whispered their Amens, joining Father Echevarría's. Etervina sobbed and rested on the embrace of her children. Pale and overcame with grief, she placed a bouquet of white and pink tobacco flowers on Antonio's tomb, as she cherished the many times he had brought her the same flowers since he was a child.

Manuel stood back silent, tears down his wrinkled and sun-weathered cheeks, visibly consumed, wondering what he could have done differently to divert his son's fate.

Antonio had returned home at last, but not as they all had hoped.

As the crowd dissipated, Etervina went ahead with her children and some others. Manuel asked to stay behind, wanting to spend a few more moments alone by his son's grave. He placed his hand over the recently sealed tombstone and prayed for his son's soul and for his family to reach some sense of peace.

He also prayed for Bessie and her family. What his son had done was terrible. How could he ever find peace? Will God ever forgive him?

Suddenly, the strangest eerie feeling overcame him. He knew he was not alone.

266

Manuel raised his eyes and saw the foggy silhouette of a woman. As she approached, he noticed that she was dressed in a long white dress, wearing an elegant white hat decorated with delicate black flowers. She was of stunning beauty.

He noticed the woman dried the tears coming down her cheeks with a lace handkerchief. He did not know her, but her appearance suggested she was American.

As she walked towards Antonio's tomb, Manuel felt compelled to uncover the woman's identity.

"Meesses, who are ju?" he said to the young woman, in broken English.

"My name is Bessie," she responded in a soft and calm tone.

Manuel was speechless.

"I came to bring you the peace you seek," she said.

As Manuel's eyes fixed on the vision, his heartbeat began to slow down. Her presence was calming.

"Forgiveness!" Manuel said.

"He has been forgiven," the angelic apparition responded. "He is resting in peace now," she said.

Manuel softly sighed, but spoke nothing. Before he could say a word, the vision vanished.

"*¡Era un buen hombre! ¡Su mente lo abandonó! ¡Perdió su libre albedrío!* He was a good man! His mind abandoned him! He lost his free will!" Manuel said to the wind, hoping it carried his message to Bessie.

The *flamboyanes* responded. Their sways cradled Manuel through his journey back home.

Manuel awoke, still in a daze, and reality sunk in.

It was all but a dream. His son's body had not yet arrived from New York.

There was much work ahead. The seedlings needed to be transplanted to the field, and harvest season was around the corner.

But Manuel was exhausted. It was still dark. He closed his eyes again.

The *coquí* sounds were soothing.

Chapter 63. Life After Antonio

Antonio's death drew the lifeblood away from his father Manuel, and it devastated his mother Etervina. Manuel could not recover from the heavy blow. But Manuel did not depart this earth without leaving a legacy.

Manuel Pontón's agricultural business records were part of the factual evidence used to convey the economic viability of the island in support of a Congressional bill for United States Citizenship for the people of Puerto Rico, originally led by Puerto Rico's Resident Commissioner to Congress, Luis Muñoz Rivera. This bill resulted in the passing of the *Jones-Shafroth Act* in March 2, 1917, granting the much-awaited citizenship to Puerto Ricans. The Congressional report lists Manuel Pontón Fernández as owning 506 acres of land, mostly dedicated to tobacco and coffee, along with property and structures, with a total assessed value of $17,280.

Regretfully, Resident Commissioner Luis Muñoz Rivera did not live to see for himself the fruits of his labor towards United States Citizenship for Puerto Ricans. He died of cancer on November 15, 1916, ten months after Antonio's execution.

. . .

Manuel Pontón Fernández passed away on Tuesday, January 21, 1919 at 7:30 p.m., three years and 14 days after his son Antonio was executed. He was 63 years old. Dr. Lavandero reported the cause of death as "nephritis," a severe infection of the kidneys. At the time he closed his eyes for good, Manuel lived with his wife Etervina in Eduardo Georgetti Street #3 in Comerío. Manuel's son Manolo signed his death certificate. Álvaro Rivera Rivera and José Juan Mandes were witnesses. Manuel was buried at the town's cemetery next to his dead children, Antonio and Etervina.

Etervina found strength on her remaining children, and in particular on her daughter Mercedes and her husband, a Spaniard by the name of Sandalio García San Julián, who welcomed Etervina in their home for many years after Manuel passed. She also lived with her son Sixto for some time. In 1943, Etervina died of lung cancer in San Juan. She was 80 years of age.

. . .

Three decades of destruction followed Puerto Rico's transition from a Spanish to a United States colony. After the World War I campaign, a great fire consumed the town of Comerío. Four major hurricanes, a tsunami and an earthquake followed the fire, all arriving in tandem with the wave of *The Great Depression*.

Two hundred and thirty six thousand Puerto Ricans in the island registered for the *World War I Draft* and 18,000 served in the war, most of them at the front lines of battle. It is said that the first United States World War I shot was fired from *El Morro Castle* in San Juan in 1915 against a German supply vessel, well before the United States entered the conflict in 1917.

The Great Depression affected Puerto Rico as it did the continental United States. Three-quarters of the island's inhabitants were considered poor.

And then came *The Great Comerío Fire of 1925*. On the night of February 24, 1925 a rabid fire devoured almost half of the small town, along with a vast majority of its historical records. The fire destroyed 133 homes. Hundreds of homeless people were relocated to temporary housing in the town's school, the Catholic Church *Santo Cristo de la Salud*, and the town's hospital. The National Guard, the Red Cross and first responders traveled all the way from San Juan and the neighboring town of Bayamón to help mitigate the flames and search for survivors under the rubble. They also secured cots, tents and other supplies. Generously, the Puerto Rican colony in New York actively fundraised for the Comerío homeless families.

The investigation revealed that the fire originated in a small store run by Emeterio Loyola from José Santiago's home. The two men were arrested for negligence and imposed a bond of $10,000. Reconstruction took years. Only 10 homes were insured.

The western part of Puerto Rico felt the tsunami and the

269

earthquake most, but the hurricanes were a different story. Arriving in July of 1926, Hurricane *San Liborio* caused vast tobacco losses. Although weaker than other hurricanes that would follow, its 66 miles-per-hour winds destroyed the tobacco curing barns, wiping up to half of the year's harvested crop in some towns, including Comerío. On September 13, 1928 *San Felipe II*, a Category five hurricane with close to 200 miles-per-hour winds, the largest ever in Puerto Rico, decimated the island. Although the 312 casualties it brought did not compare with the more than 3,000 resulting from Hurricane *San Ciriaco* in 1899 (in part due to the new presence of a warning system) the property losses reached $50 million. The hurricane destroyed the tobacco, coffee and sugar plantations, as well as most of the shade and fruit trees, and it left over half a million people homeless, killing 29 in Comerío. Hurricane *San Nicolás* followed in 1931 and *San Ciprián* in 1932, a 120 mile-per-hour hurricane with a loss price tag of $30 million.

Thirty years of economic emergency, massive crop destruction, epidemic-level illnesses and blatant desolation.

. . .

Despite the enormous repeated calamities, Sixto Pontón continued to run his father Manuel's business and tend his land. Some of the land had been split among the children in years past and some had been sold to the *Puerto Rico Leaf Tobacco Company*.

It was not the same with Manuel gone. Nothing was ever the same since Antonio died.

With increased production, the price of tobacco began declining. In 1931, "*Los Caballeros de la Noche*" (The Knights of the Night) pressured the planters to stop planting, with the idea of reducing output and increasing prices. Under the movement of *La No Siembra* (The Non-Planting), anyone who planted would be subject to crop loss, as *los caballeros* and others would enter the premises and pull any plants from the soil. Not much could be done.

In 1935, Sixto appeared in the *United States Agricultural Special Census of Puerto Rico* as landlord of 200 *cuerdas* (about 194 acres) of land in Comerío, which he managed since 1919 (the year Manuel passed). From the 200 *cuerdas,* about 76 were cultivated. The land's value was listed as $12,000, and it was mortgaged for $8,900. There were 22 structures on the land, used for farming and homes for the family and their workers. There were "33 white people and 30 colored people" reported to live in those structures.

The 200 *cuerdas* were split between two town sectors or *barrios*: 130 *cuerdas* in barrio *Palomas* and 70 *cuerdas* in barrio *Naranjo*. The following was reported as the harvest from the cultivated land in 1935. (After the United States occupation, one quintal became equivalent to one hundredweight):

"corn (16 cuerdas, 64 quintals); rice (2 cuerdas, 3 quintals); beans (12 cuerdas, 30 quintals); pigeon peas (2 cuerdas, 3 quintals); "Guinea Grass" (3 cuerdas, 2000 bundles); batatas (12 cuerdas, 600 quintals); yautía (2 cuerdas, 80 quintals); coffee (16 cuerdas, 500 quintals, number of coffee trees 4,800); tobacco (27 cuerdas, 1,890 quintals)

Tropical Fruit: bananas (8000 trees in production, 3000 not in production, 5000 bundles); plantains (1000 trees in production, 300 not in production, 700 bundles); oranges (20 trees in production, 10 not in production, 20 boxes.)

Animals: 3 horses, 2 calves, 4 bulls, 6 oxen, 4 cows (producing 1,200 quarts of milk), 8 pigs and 8 chicken."

Sixto stopped working in 1936 when he fell ill with severe stomach pains. He passed away in the summer of 1937 of post-operatory shock while being intervened for stomach cancer at the *Clínica García Díaz* (today known as *Hospital Pavía*.) He was 46.

Manolo continued working his own land until 1925, when he retired. He lost his battle with cancer on January of 1947, at 65 years old. An aggressive skin tumor that began on his nose five years earlier took his life. When he signed Manolo's United States draft registration in 1942, government recorder Epifanio Fiz Jiménez noted that Manolo was missing part of his nose.

Mercedes moved to San Juan with her husband and two children. She died in 1971 at 75 years of age.

After finishing high school, Antonio's son Manolo moved to New York to join his brother Antonio, Jr. and their mother. He later married there. Antonio, Jr. returned to Puerto Rico with his mother, fought in World War II as a sergeant of the United States Army, married and had a family.

. . .

The Puerto Rican tobacco production began to decline as a result of a change in market demand preference from cigars to cigarettes. Puerto Rico transitioned from an agricultural into an industrial economy as part of *Operación Manos a la Obra* (Operation Bootstrap), introduced by the government in 1948. In 2010, Reynolds American, Inc. (the second largest manufacturer of tobacco products in the world) closed its manufacturing plants in Puerto Rico. To date, *Don Collins* cigars are still manufactured in San Juan.

. . .

With the passage of time, Manuel's land was sold, and the old Comerío cemetery, holding the remains of Manuel Pontón Fernández and his two children Etervina and Antonio, was abandoned and forgotten, erased by the elements. A new cemetery opened in 1930, and two others followed after 1980. The town was rebuilt over the years. Recently, a school and a hospital were constructed over the sacred grounds of the abandoned burial site.

In Comerío, Manuel Pontón Fernández, the Asturian child immigrant who traveled by water to Puerto Rico and became a prominent Comerío tobacco planter at the turn of the 20th century, is now but a faded memory consumed by fire, as his son Antonio.

But Manuel Pontón's spirit still lives. He lives in the *Río La Plata,* at the bed of the steep mountains once covered with tobacco snow, and in the *coquí* whistles. He lives in the swaying leaves of the Comerío *flamboyanes* whispering *"¡La tierra no se acaba!* The land does not perish!" He lives in the breeze carrying his prayer for "Forgiveness!" on behalf of a son who lost his will.

FIN

ME VOY PORQUE LA TIERRA YA NO ES MÍA
Porque mis pies están cansados,
mis ojos ciegos
mi boca seca,
y mi cuerpo dócil y ligero,
para entrar en el aire.
Me voy porque ya no hay caminos para mí en el suelo.
Salí del agua, he vivido en la sangre
y ahora me espera el viento
para llevarme al sol ...
Salí del mar ... y acabaré en el fuego.

- Segmento de "Me Voy," poema de León Felipe

Afternote

I was a man whose will abandoned him in the darkest of times. I was sick with an inherited ailment and an incurable disease. I lost control of my actions and fell through the cracks of justice.

I was wrongfully executed. Let the world know that I was innocent by reason of insanity and that the American Justice System, driven by imperfect men and imperfect laws failed me miserably. And so it has failed many others.

One hundred years after the event that marked my doom, our legal system is supposed to have evolved. But has it?

The American Justice System has progressed some since 1915. The *Hearsay Rules* often close the door to unreliable evidence in the courtroom, and *Miranda Rights* now exist to inform a criminal defendant that he is entitled to counsel if he chooses, before he speaks a word or subjects to a search of his person or property. Search warrants add another safeguard. I am thrilled to see that the strict *M'Naghten Rule* was eventually deemed to be an unfair law to mentally ill defendants, that today society better understands the mind (although there is a long way to go in this area), that discrimination is not as rampant in the courtroom (although it remains ever present), and that there are more safeguards in place before the claws of society put a human being to death.

However, even with a century of lessons learned building the résumé of the American Justice System, innocent people are still convicted, executions continue, and worst of all, innocent people are still being executed.

Today, New York no longer supports the death penalty. That's one step forward, although a little too late for me. Modern so-called "more humane" methods of execution, like cyanide gas and the lethal injection, have clearly failed. Look at the latest botched executions to see what I mean, if you don't believe me. And Virginia, do you really

275

want to return to *La Silla Eléctrica* (The Electric Chair)? What are you thinking? Many steps back.

History has demonstrated that the death penalty is an abomination. It was a blot on civilization a century ago, and it continues to be a blot today. It does not work to deter crime, it cannot be reconciled with religious beliefs, and it is economically prohibitive.

Here is a suggestion: Focus on understanding and treating mental illness, focus on crime prevention and education, instead. Let's talk in another hundred years from now.

My will failed me a century ago, but today my will, my legacy, is that my story of injustice serves to protect the rights of others, so that they do not have to endure what I suffered, what my family suffered, what my whole island suffered.

My story has been told. The world now knows the truth about the injustices committed against me.

I rest in peace.

Yours,

José Antonio Pontón Santiago

Author's Note

This is the story of the self-made tobacco planter and *industrial* (businessman) Manuel Pontón Fernández, who in 1870 emigrated as a young boy from Asturias, Spain to Comerío, Puerto Rico, and of his son José Antonio, who in 1911 went to study at Albany Law School, fell in love, and in 1916 became the first Puerto Rican and the first Hispanic person executed on the electric chair in the United States.

While endeavoring into a historical journey of places, people and events spanning three countries and over a century, *Antonio's Will* provides an account of Antonio Pontón's family, life, imprisonment, trial and execution by electrocution and suggests that Antonio Pontón was executed wrongfully. Antonio Pontón, the son of a prominent Puerto Rican family, committed the dreadful act of killing, forced by the insanity that robbed him of his free will.

In addition to clear evidence of a family history of mental illness, Antonio suffered from a disease that invaded his brain and rendered him insane. However, New York prosecutors, politicians, judges and the jury could not afford not to execute the young Puerto Rican law student. An environment filled with bias, ignorance and taboo, along with the flawed laws of the times and the courts' failure to apply due constitutional protections to Antonio, trumped justice and due process.

Yes, Antonio brutally murdered another human being. But four renowned doctors diagnosed his mental illness. He provided the family history and the blood test evidence to prove it. Antonio Pontón should have been sent to a mental institution and treated for his disease. Instead, he was executed, the victim of "The Perfect Storm" that deprived him of the due process of law.

Over 600 persons have been convicted and executed on the electric chair in New York since Antonio Pontón's execution. Many of them were innocent or wrongfully executed. Charles Stielow, Antonio's illiterate and poverty-stricken prison mate, was one of the fortunate ones to be spared. He was eventually set free, after eighteen months of confinement in Sing Sing, and after walking the *Green Mile* a total of *five* times. On Stielow's last procession of death, only 20 minutes before the switch would have been thrown, Governor Whitman called the Sing Sing warden to halt the execution. If the true murderers had not confessed, Stielow would have joined the long list of those unjustly executed.

. . .

As depicted in *Antonio's Will*, during the early 1900's not everyone favored the death penalty or was blind to the connection between mental illness and criminality. In his book *Sing Sing Doctor* published in 1935, Dr. Amos O. Squire, Sing Sing's Chief Physician during Antonio's imprisonment and execution, expressed his strong disagreement with the New York insanity defense law of the time. He also relayed his medical opinion that illnesses such as dementia and chemical imbalances, not just the surrounding environment and educational background, could drive a person to commit the ultimate deed. "Anyone could be a criminal ... [and] none of us need to congratulate ourselves any too much on our success in keeping out of prison," he wrote.

Dr. Squire also shared that there are times in which humans do not have the ability to control their actions or discern their real nature, and the law acted unfairly in executing them. He knew this first-hand. The doctor resigned his post at Sing Sing in 1925, largely persuaded by his daughter, after she learned her father had developed a progressive anxiety about participating in executions. Dr. Squire began having involuntary impulses to touch the inmate while he was being electrocuted, and one day the impulse was so strong that the good doctor almost succeeded in crossing "to the other side" along with the condemned man. Dr. Squire was a man ahead of his time, as were Wardens Thomas Mott Osborne, George W. Kirchwey and Assistant Warden Spencer Miller, much unlike those who decided to execute Antonio Pontón.

Today, the law has evolved some and the courts have created measures to ensure constitutional safeguards to help prevent injustices such as those committed in Antonio Pontón's case. But while today there are more checks and balances than in 1915, society has still not "gotten it right." *The Case of Antonio Pontón, One Hundred Years Later*, a companion reading to *Antonio's Will*, presents arguments pointing to grave errors committed during Antonio Pontón's trial, provides a historical overview of the death penalty law and insanity defense modifications in New York, and addresses constitutional protections that have emerged since 1915 to protect criminal defendants. In addition, it presents a medical perspective on the criminal mind and also advocates for the abolition of capital punishment from ethical, constitutional and economic angles.

. . .

Antonio's Will is the result of many years of study that began with family history research. For those drawn to history, anthropology and mystery, genealogy can be a rewarding experience. It is a never-ending journey that can easily rescue a person from the typical routines of life, transporting him or her to the intriguing world of their ancestors. What seems like an "extended hobby" for many can absorb a great deal of our time, even years, as it has with me. We become investigators, history detectives; endlessly thirsty for the next clue, putting the pieces of many puzzles together, often at once. And sometimes we may not be prepared for what we uncover.

The research often feels as though watching a movie in reverse. The observer is challenged to uncover "what happened next," as the next scene of the movie already took place long ago. Often, there are no more clues, and one remains frozen in time, hoping that the vault that holds our clues hostage opens wide, setting all the inklings of evidence free for our discovery. But there is a poetic wisdom in historic research: while it often allows us to travel through hundreds of years in just days or moments, sometimes it knows to slow down our "time travel," perhaps so that we learn to value each fact discovered as it rightfully deserves.

However lengthy and frustrating it may be at times, the quest can be rewarding and exciting. With every scintilla of progress, we gain a clearer understanding of where we came from, and this information can sometimes unveil an unknown ancestor's silent legacy that helps explain why we do the things we do, why we have a specific tendency or have been gifted to be artists, craftsmen, teachers, lawyers, doctors, scientists, musicians, artisans, historians.

But most of all, this journey through time unveils history in a completely different light; it makes history personal. We learn how our distant relatives lived, their joys, their adversities, their historical and social environment, and sometimes, if we are lucky, we stumble on facts or stories that were never passed down through the generations; facts that our ancestors decided were not important; or facts that were simply lost in time, taken to the grave. These discoveries are probably those that yield the most emotional moments in our investigation.

Without having ever met them, we get to know our ancestors. We share with them in a different dimension in time, like a science-fiction movie of sorts. And we are privileged, because then we truly realize how important the life of every single human being is, however imperfect or short-lived, and how without this human chain and every historical fact that surrounded the people who served as the chain's links, we would not be here today. So, we honor our ancestors and we honor our history.

Some time ago, while researching one of my father's Puerto Rican lines at the turn of the century, originating from the Spanish region of Asturias, I came across one of those stories never passed down. As I traced the line further and continued turning stones and mining information, it became apparent that I had uncovered a tragic event of great importance, not only to my family, but also to Puerto Rican and Hispanic history. This information was unknown to my father and his siblings, although it was reason for front-page newspaper headlines in the early 1900's, both in the United States and in Puerto Rico. Consequently, I decided this finding needed extended research, and that the story should be shared beyond my immediate family. And so, I poured my soul into this project.

While the historical facts in this book are non-fiction, I took the liberty of injecting some fictional elements, representing my imagination of certain aspects of the characters' lives and interactions. Fiction is present, for example, in the details of Manuel Pontón Fernández' journey to Puerto Rico and his first letter home, which I wrote inspired by dozens of letters penned by other immigrants like him; in my envisioning of Manuel's experiences as he adapted to the culture and traditions of Puerto Rico; in the exchanges between Antonio and his parents at the Port of San Juan; in the exchanges between Manuel and Etervina; in the events and exchanges that took place at Schoharie between Antonio, Bessie, Mrs. Kromer and others; in the exchange between Antonio and Bessie at Coney Island when they discussed the unfortunate fate of Topsy, the electrocuted elephant and Antonio's alter ego; in the exchanges between Antonio and his parents and others while he was a student at Albany Law School; and in the events back in Comerío when Manuel dreamt about Antonio's funeral procession and burial, when he had a vision of Bessie. Antonio's personal experiences in New York, for example, during walks from his apartment to school, in the classroom, and during sightseeing trips are also fictional, but they were based on carefully researched locations, events, timings and other historical information. The events surrounding his execution are factual, but for the dialogue and environment created to convey the anguish he likely felt. His last words are real.

We will probably never know for sure what really transpired in the characters' minds, other than what they have revealed themselves or has been documented through newspapers, letters, books and other media. We have yet to uncover additional factual and historical information. I say "we," as I am hoping that if any relatives or descendants of the characters, or anyone who reads this book, has additional relevant information they can share on the subject, they will bring it to light. Historical research never ends. The book's website (www.AntoniosWill.com) will relay any new information and discoveries.

. . .

While I am publishing the scholarly research behind this novel separately, I feel compelled to share some important sources that helped me understand and bring to life the story behind *Antonio's Will*. The story's non-fictional framework and historical detail were pieced together using secondary (published) and primary (oral) sources. In the information age, the Internet was an invaluable research resource.

About 2,000 references, including books, articles, blogs, court records, vital records, cemetery burial records, prison records, passenger manifests, military muster rolls, property, land and tax records, census, newspapers, letters, telegrams and other communications, government documents, yearbooks, university catalogs, photographs, maps, and other references, as well as my own oral interviews and written exchanges, assisted me in shaping the story and helped me present the factual, cultural and historical framework as I engaged in storytelling.

The early history of Puerto Rico is well documented in a diversity of publications. One of the most fascinating early accounts of Spain's colonization of the island is revealed in *Las Obras del Obispo D. Fray Bartolomé de las Casas* (1552) where Spanish Catholic Bishop Las Casas relays his first-hand observations of the colonization efforts, the discovery of Puerto Rico, its Taíno Indian inhabitants and their culture, and their unjust decimation by the colonizers. Another invaluable historical resource is Salvador Brau's *Puerto Rico y su Historia, Investigaciones Críticas* (1894). Both references are available in digital form via *Google Books*, which holds an ample digital library of public domain materials.

Numerous publications addressing the history of tobacco, the industry and its development in Puerto Rico, particularly in the town of *Comerío*, assisted in my understanding of Manuel Pontón Fernández' business environment and life, including the art, science and excruciating work behind tobacco farming. The book by Epifanio Fiz Jiménez, *Comerío y su Gente: datos históricos, estampas de mi pueblo, datos geográficos*, Barcelona: Ediciones Rumbos (1957) provided insight about Manuel's arrival to Comerío. The *Archivo General de Puerto Rico* (Puerto Rico's General Archives) holds many treasures that helped shed light into Manuel Pontón and his business affairs. Historical commercial bulletins promoted him as a business owner, and turn-of-the-century United States Congressional reports listed him among the most prominent landowners in Puerto Rico in 1917.

The *Archivo Histórico Nacional de España* (Spain's Historical National Archives) and its online PARES database (http://pares.mcu.es) maintains a vast online repository of historical documents including original colonial Spanish government documents reflecting, for example, Crown travel allowances, taxpayer lists, elections information, census and legal documents relevant to Spain and its colonies. The *Archivo Militar de Madrid* (Spain's

Military Archives) (http://www.portalcultura.mde.es) is an excellent source of military information relevant to the Spanish-American war events in Puerto Rico.

Genealogical/family history databases were key to identifying people, family relationships, places, dates and events. The *Ancestry.com* commercial database is a key genealogical investigative resource containing ships manifests with passenger lists, United States Census and military references, birth and death documents, some newspapers, and among many other valuable resources, a recently-added searchable "Puerto Rico civil records birth, marriage and death library" offered in partnership with *FamilySearch.org* that I wish I had access to during my early years of manual research!

FamilySearch.org, a free online database hosted by The Mormon Church of Latter-Day Saints (LDS), also provides census and other vital information, but its most resourceful assets for my particular research were the digitized Puerto Rican Catholic Church and civil birth, marriage and death books and records. For the most part, the records must be browsed page by page, amounting to an arduous research task (particularly when most of the books lack indexes and many are almost illegible, water-stained, torn or destroyed by termites.)

However, the valuable information is preserved and accessible online, saving much time when compared to the early days, where researchers had to conduct all their investigations onsite in churches, courthouses and other public offices, often having to wait months to secure permissions from government and/or church officials to access the valuable informational assets. Often, I undertook this quest to no avail. While it remains the case still in many towns and venues, and I have had to endure some of this painful aspect of research (as many other researchers have) *FamilySearch.org* has proven to be an invaluable resource to lift the barriers of access to many historical documents. The LDS effort is an enormous contribution to worldwide history and genealogy.

Numerous newspapers, particularly the *Schenectady Gazette*, the *Albany Evening Journal,* and the *Amsterdam Daily Democrat and Recorder*, Puerto Rico newspapers such as *La Democracia, El Tiempo* and *El Mundo*, along with New York case reporters and prison reports, contain useful information regarding the events culminating in the murder, Antonio Pontón's incarceration, trial and appeals, including statements made by Antonio, police officers, doctors, trial witnesses, judge, attorneys, the governor, among many others. The newspapers also provided some highlights of the massive public support and repeated efforts to persuade the governor and the courts to commute Antonio's death sentence.

The *New York Times* and *the Evening Herald* provided details about the unfortunate electrocution of Topsy the elephant, Antonio's alter ego. Newspaper and supplementary trial transcript research revealed key nuggets of information about Harry K. Thaw's trials, as well as the lives of doctors, judges, wardens, professors, deans, criminals, executions, and other real characters and events in the story.

Writings by those who witnessed first-hand the daily turn of events at the Sing Sing Prison, shedding light on aspects of Antonio Pontón's execution, unveiled key insights for storytelling. The book *Sing Sing Doctor*, by Dr. Amos O. Squire, narrated the doctor's experiences as Sing Sing Prison Chief Physician from 1914 to 1925, opening the door to his mind, providing details about Sing Sing prison life, and revealing his own theories of medicine relevant to criminology.

Exclusive press interviews provided by Charles Stielow, the man who spent 18 months in Sing Sing while Antonio was there, and George B. Meserole, the former Sing Sing prison officer who labored for more than four decades at the penitentiary, both witnesses to the day of Antonio's execution, offered painful and eerie accounts of the last moments of Antonio Pontón's life. They also provided insight into the prison environment and the torment endured by death row prisoners.

Mark Essig's *Edison and the Electric Chair: A Story of Light and Death,* Bloomsbury Publishing (2009), provided a well-presented and superbly researched account of the history of the Electric Chair, including Thomas Edison's involvement in its development and the gruesome history of human suffering caused by the process of execution by electrocution. Over a dozen other references supplemented my education on this subject.

New York state archives, historical societies, medical societies, special collections, and "Who's Who" historical publications, among others, helped add dimension to the characters and detail to the events of the times. Rutger's University's Collection of *Edison's Papers* provided insight into Edison's son William. These sources also presented an opportunity to juxtapose William L. Edison with Harry K. Thaw and Antonio Pontón as children of wealthy hardworking men who, aside from any potential present mental illness or other influences, appear to have given their children all, while perhaps doing them a disservice in the process.

Case law and governmental reports available in the public domain, as well as modern news reports, provided a historical timeline of the death penalty, its impact on society and on individuals related to victims and defendants, as well as offered a window to United States and global perspectives regarding capital punishment. The *Death Penalty Information Center* (www.deathpenaltyinfo.org) proved an excellent resource for data and statistics on the subject, keeping a repository of historic and modern executions, general publications, as well as updated information on the death penalty in the United States, broken down by state and territories.

The *Center for Puerto Rican Studies* at Hunter College, City University of New York (http://centropr.hunter.cuny.edu) holds a *United States Identification* database with valuable information that helped me open a window to an important character life milestone.

Genealogy associations are an invaluable resource for building networks and meeting other individuals with similar interests, as well as for sharing information. *The Puerto Rican Genealogical Society* (http://www.genealogiapr.com) for example, makes available valuable general publications and resources. Some of its members were graciously willing to assist me in locating references and shared information when specifically solicited. This resource is particularly helpful with out-of-print books, as many of the members have built their own libraries over the years.

While the world of the Internet is an invaluable and powerful engine to access information, a considerable portion of my time was invested on interviews, on the phone, emailing, faxing, writing letters, and visiting libraries and other venues in an effort to gather and verify information and reach out to individuals and organizations that could share golden facts that I could later connect together to derive stories. This was a time-consuming and sometimes costly aspect of my self-financed research, but it was critical in order to corroborate facts, uncover new information and provide a richer dimension to the stories. Many walls remain standing, preventing the extraction of additional information, for now.

Before I conclude, I cannot emphasize enough the value of oral history. We take for granted the stories in the minds of our parents and grandparents, aunts and uncles, elder cousins, distant relatives or even those who knew our family. But when our loved ones pass or when age or illness unmercifully erases their memories, the stories in their minds abandon us. We should work to note down, record and document their stories and preserve their photographs, letters and historical documents. These are part of our history and our heritage. This task has become much easier with today's technology. We should leverage this privilege.

. . .

I hope my main contribution in writing *Antonio's Will* does not stop at telling the story of the rise to success of Manuel Pontón Fernández, the unfortunate fate of his son Antonio, and the history and the stories surrounding theirs. While I consider sharing these accounts important, my wish is that the book also invites you, the reader, to engage in learning about your history and research your own ancestry, and I hope this brings you closer to your heritage and your culture.

There are many new stories to discover and many remain to be told. Let us all participate in uncovering "what happened next."

Yasmin Tirado-Chiodini, 2014

Notes

Made in the USA
Middletown, DE
05 August 2021